MOTION

VISION+VALUE SERIES

THE NATURE AND ART
OF
MOTION

EDITED BY
GYORGY KEPES

George Braziller, New York

Copyright © 1965 GEORGE BRAZILLER, INC.

All rights reserved.

For information address the publisher:

George Braziller, Inc.

1 Park Avenue

New York, New York 10016

Library of Congress Catalog Card number: 65–10807

Fourth Printing

Manufactured in the United States of America

CONTENTS

The inescapable attribute of our time is its runaway pace. Tidal waves of traffic pound us; sprawling cities and exploding populations squeeze us. Wildly erratic throbbing migrations—the daily shuttle from home to work, from work to home, the weekend surge from city to country and from country to city, the punctuations of rush-hour deadlocks—toss us in an accelerating rhythm barely within our control. Streams of speeding objects—motorcars, airplanes, intercontinental missiles, orbiting space capsules—weave a rapidly changing fabric all around us with patterns of spiraling velocities. At night, the reassuring calm of the firmament is blotted out by our cities, which are transformed into giant circuses where darting headlights, winking traffic lights, glittering, gaudy displays, and advertising signs whirl and swirl and pirouette in frantic competition for our attention.

The traffic of the outside world has its inner counterpart. Our interior world is shaped by the restless haste of bad consciences. We conceive friendships, set goals, and establish values in a relentless hurry. Compulsively, we try to perform faster, produce more, acquire power and possessions that corrupt and corrode us. Our proudest and most potent possessions, without reliable social guidance, become misused. We live under the terrifying shadow of superinventions, with their much too easy push-button control. As we all know so well, these have brought us to the brink of final disaster.

Is there any escape? Can we step outside our rushed selves and find the calm in which to meet our neglected deeper needs? As well step out of a racing express train without expectation of harm! It seems equally impossible to look inside ourselves and find renewal of spirit. Our privacy, the sanctuary for our imaginative powers, is invaded, not only by such lashing tentacles of this world of motion as the onrushing images of the television screen, but even more by our own frantic restlessness.

In spite of all this oscillating traffic, many of us feel that a change, a true change in our human situation, has not come about. Motion, in a strict physical sense, is change of position with respect to a reference system of space coordinates. In a broad social sense, motion is change with respect to a reference system of basic human values. In this sense, we find ourselves trapped in a gigantic social and emotional traffic jam. Just as our cities are strangled by traffic because vehicles overflow our streets, so our vast traffic of new knowledge and power is choking to a standstill.

If, by some sudden magic, we were to live a million times more rapidly than we do, in surroundings that retained their present pace, then the coming and going of day and night, the slowest movements of a sleeping child, would become a blur, a texture too smooth to be grasped by the senses. We experience the opposite of this. Events today appear to be accelerating insanely, as if we were living a million times more slowly among objects whirling beyond the threshold of our control.

The last accelerated decades of history span what used to be centuries of technical progress and centuries of economic and social advancement or regression. On the one hand, tribal communities from isolated corners of the world have moved, within a few years, to membership in the supranational world organization; on the other, nations with centuries of civilized living have shed civilized habits and relapsed into the lowest, most brutal level of human existence.

A feeling of hopelessness has seized our most sensitive and best equipped minds. Their clearest purposes and most passionate efforts have become mockeries. They despair because they believe that individual efforts and achievements are too few and slow to alter massive social events. The individual's role seems meaningless, out of scale with the pace of happenings.

Unable to correlate the time scale of the individual's willed purposes with the time scale of social directions, others of us blame a hundred different things: events occur absurdly fast; the world is absurdly big; power is absurdly concentrated; life is absurdly short; machines and techniques overshadow humans. At a crazy tempo, we shift scapegoats without realizing that the real problem is our lack of a coordinating, genuinely contemporary, dynamic scale.

We should understand that this dizzying, runaway environment is just the final wild reverberation of a long-evolving change in the foundation of our knowledge and system of values. Not least among its roots is change in our scientific understanding of motion.

Interpretation of physical motion has had a seminal role in science and technology. Galileo's study of falling bodies established the solid foundation of our scientific understanding of physical nature. Outstanding scientific achievements of the seventeenth century were based upon interpretation of planetary motion. The infinitesimal calculus, the mathematical tool that was decisive in the shaping of our scientific and technical world, grew out of investigation of change of motion. In our century, the constancy of the velocity of light is fundamental to the new physics.

The increasing precision of man's understanding of motion in the physical world has led to recognition of motion as a pervasive aspect of nature. In our new conceptual models of nature, the stable, solid world of substance which in the past was considered permanent and preordained, is understood as widely dispersed fields of dynamic energies. Matter—the tangible, visible, stable substance in the old image of the physical world—is recast today as an invisible web of nuclear events with orbiting electrons jumping from orbit to orbit.

Paralleling the dissolution of the old notion of matter is a fundamental transformation of our ideas about men and society. Darwinian evolution, the social theories of the mid-nineteenth century, and this century's Freudian revolution have led to a reformulation of our concepts of geological, biological, psychological, and social nature. We have learned to recognize that matter, the earth, the human body, the human psyche, and social and cultural ideas are all in continuous transformation.

The key problem of motion is still in the forefront of contemporary knowledge. How to detach electrons from their parent atoms and how to control their movements are central problems of physics. How to guide the movement of light waves, radio waves, and waves of electricity along their innumerable paths is the key technical problem of communication. How to move individuals to recognize the heartbeat of our time, how to move human sensibilities to respond in an affirmative, creative way to challenges of today are key problems of social communication, and, thus, of creative vision.

Perceptual studies have revealed a paradox that shapes creative vision and illuminates its fundamental character. The patterns of optical signals that touch our retina and consequently reach the brain are never static. They are compound patterns of complex mobile configurations. They change with the ever-changing light of nature. The path of the moving sun, the passing clouds, and other mobile sources of illumination constantly model and remodel the forms in the environment. This ceaselessly changing illumination reveals a continuously moving, continuously transforming world of objects. Things grow and disintegrate; they change their shapes, size and position relative to themselves, to each other, and to us. These dynamics of the outside spatial world are amplified within us by our never-resting eyes, which are carried by our moving head and moving body. But in spite of all this mobility, the essential characteristic of the world as we perceive it is, in fact, *constancy* and *stability*.

ii

The world as we perceive it is made up of things with persisting identity, existing in a frame of reference of stationary space. Motionless objects, as we have said, are perceived as though flat, and only when the eye receives a successive flow of light patterns reflected from an object can we recognize depth and detect the object's three-dimensional extension. The changing position of our eyes relative to an object reveals its characteristic three-dimensional "thingness".

This paradox has its inversion. Stationary photographs of successive views of moving objects projected at the frequency at which they were taken are perceived as though the object were moving. Changing patterns of successive stationary retinal stimulation inevitably induce an experience of motion. There is, thus, a fundamental figure-ground relationship of constancy and change. One does not exist without the other. Together, they build all the figures of our experience.

The role of motion as a generator of vision and insight has still further implications. Psychologists have observed that such conceptual constants as, say, "mechanical causality", are rooted in the concrete motion experiences of early childhood. A child becomes aware of the idea of causality when he himself causes things to move by pushing, pulling, building, and breaking things. Such movements occur by chance at first; then the child recognizes and exploits this chance, and produces changes based upon full awareness of causal connections.

The dynamic unity of constancy and change has a fundamental role in our intellectual growth. Our clearest understanding of the nature of these complementary opposites has been reached through grasp of the principle of self-regulating systems.

We have learned to understand the inner working of processes: how our own body stabilizes and regulates itself between extremes of temperature or other physiological conditions. If we are too hot, our body reacts to bring on conditions that return us toward our standard temperature; we do the same when we feel too cold, hungry, tired, or unhappy. There are certain danger limits of the body and the mind, the individual and the society, that endanger their existence when overstepped. And life in this sense signifies a chain of actions and reactions, challenge and response, aiming for survival, which means, on a higher level, also physical, moral, and intellectual growth. If such controlled growth is intercepted by extreme challenge, serious harm could result. Recent studies reveal that when people are kept for a prolonged duration in a completely homogenous, unvarying environment, they suffer from visual and auditory hallucinations, and, after being released, may still carry scars of sensory deprivation from their prison. On the other hand, there is overwhelming evidence that when confronted with a task beyond the limits of our capacity to perceive and understand, we undergo a complete bewilderment, which may climax in catastrophic breakdown.

A jittery compulsion about some component aspects of our total field is characteristic of our contemporary art. We have lost a sense of inner guidance,.and the pattern of our visual creativity has no logic. We single out fragments of aspects unrelated to what happened before or what may happen tomorrow. We busily improvise a mythology of speed, forgetting repose, introspection, the deeper anchors of a fuller life.

The nausea that pervades the work of many of our best writers, poets, and artists is like motion sickness. It is caused by unguided, frequently repeated changes of velocity and direction and our consequent failure to adapt ourselves to the suddenly changing stimulation. Our sickening psychological and social disorientation, with its attitudes against life and art, is due partly to the unguided sequence of our environmental changes, our knowledge and equipment, and partly to a lack of adaptation to the sudden, violent jerks and thrusts of our self-induced but uncontrolled conditions. We have learned to telescope time conceptually and technically, but evidently failed to do so emotionally and socially.

Some fifty years ago, the Italian Futurist Marinetti babbled about "the racing space, the acrobatic somersault, the slap in the face and the blow of the fist—war, the bloody and necessary test of the people's force." His immature cult of crude sensations, his adulation of the dynamic hardware of the twentieth century—the car, the machine gun, the airplane—was well answered by Gabo and Pevsner:

"The pompous slogan of 'Speed' was played from the hands of the Futurists as a great trump . . . But ask any Futurist how does he imagine 'speed', and there will emerge a whole arsenal of frenzied automobiles, rattling railway depots, snarled wires, the clank and the noise and the clang of carouselling streets . . . does one really need to convince them that all that is not necessary for speed and for its rhythms?

"Look at a ray of sun . . . the stillest of the still forces; it speeds more than 300 kilometres in a second . . . behold our starry firmament . . . who hears it . . . and yet what are our depots to those depots of the Universe: What are our earthly trains to those hurrying trains of the galaxies?"*

The challenge of the new cannot be met merely by giving three cheers for whatever is new. Grown-ups cannot be satisfied by the hot-rodder's aimless pavement scorching, nor be as happy as a child with the bang of a firecracker or the swoops of a roller-coaster ride. Mere identification with the novelty of immediate visual dynamics without an understanding of their roots and their direction of growth only prevents us from finding the way out of our present blind alleys. Some attempts to come to terms with the impacts of our explosive world have bogged down in just such easy-to-come-by excitement. The central interest of many artists has been riveted to the exhilarating dynamic visual aspect of our surroundings. But other artists have searched with admirable discipline for visual idioms capable of expressing the kinetic character of their experience.

First chronologically, as well as in significance, were artists working in the early part of this century. Painters and sculptors called the Cubists realized that the visual nature of our environment cannot be projected in an artistic image seen from a single fixed view. The visual image is not a mirror of something fixed outside, but the far more complex product of a creative process. The Cubist artist's painted image of physical space was not the painted replica of his optical image. It was an evocation and order of the changing vistas collected by his moving, exploring eyes. The Cubists recognized consciously what creative vision has been by instinct since men first became image makers.

Their efforts led to the rediscovery of the fundamental aspects of artistic vision: *complementary unity*—of the observer and the observed, of order and vitality, of constancy and change; *rhythm*—basic to all living process, and so, too, to the creation or reliving of an artistic configuration; *sequence* in the life span of created experience. Images are created and perceived as structured sequences of patterns; melodic line, contrapuntal organization, are inherent not only in musical patterning but in all created forms.

Today this basic knowledge has a new, more precise, and more embracing significance. Not only artists but scientists also have come to recognize that they cannot create a valid model of nature that exists independently of the observer. Complementarity is accepted as basic in the description of

*Naum Gabo and Noton Pevsner. *The Realistic Manifesto*, 1920.

natural phenomena. There is always a pair of interacting aspects: the outside world and the process of observation. In their different ways, scientists and artists both recognize this fundamental complementary relationship. Their recent revolutionary contribution has been to recognize the dynamic interpenetration of the outside and the inside world. The basis of the creative dialogue between observed and observer is movement, including the time factor in the observer's experience.

But the Cubists also recognized that the invariant aspects of the continuously shifting world are as essential as the exploratory movements of our eyes in making this world legible, meaningful, and manageable. Juan Gris, a rare, disciplined mind, summed it up as follows:

"By way of natural reaction against the fugitive elements employed by the Impressionists, painters felt the need to discover less unstable elements in the objects to be represented. And they chose that category of elements which remains in the mind through apprehension and is not continually changing. For the momentary effects of light they substituted, for example, what they believed to be the local colors of objects. For the visual appearance of a form they substituted what they believed to be the actual quality of this form."*

This fundamental understanding was bypassed by the artists who followed the Cubists. The Futurists were typical. They closed their eyes to their inner world, and focused on the dynamic outside environment. They were Italians, living in a country lagging behind industrially and blinded by past glories, a country of museums, with little relevance for twentieth-century man seeking his identity. They assumed that the two worlds of the old and the new could not coexist and, rejecting their heritage, blasted away at all the inhibiting memories of the past. They used techniques of the visual recording of moving objects that closely resembled the photographic motion studies of the great nineteenth-century physiologist E. J. Marey, and claimed them as art-saving, revolutionary innovations. They claimed complete authority for this one-sided vision, and denied existence to other forms of visual expression.

In the same way that the Futurists were blind to the past, a more recent group of artists has been blind to the future. They have renounced the public forum and recoiled to the innermost privacy of unsharable singular moments of existence. They shrink the world to a rebellious gesture, to violent graphs of the cornered man. "The big moment came," as an articulate spokesman of this group has put it, "when it was decided to paint . . . just to paint. The gesture on the canvas was a gesture of liberation from value—political, aesthetic, moral." But, in fact, these artists recoil from the necessary vital dialogue with the outside environment and, thus, have broken again the essential unity of the seer and the seen.

The interest of a new group of motion-addicted artists has swung back again to the outside world. But, instead of looking for new qualities of twentieth-century life, they produce substitute moving objects, either cerebral, impeccable, watchwork-like toy machines, or self-destructive Frankenstein monsters made from corroded fragments of industrial waste. Some painters also experiment with motion, and their sophisticated knowledge of visual illusions produces amusing, well-groomed eye teasers by mobilizing every possible optical trick to animate surfaces into virtual motion.

The most recent group of artists has returned from kinetic images to concrete objects in their environment. They have become fascinated by vulgar features of everyday life, and have chosen them as emblems. Seductive selling devices of the competitive society—advertising pictures, containers,

*Juan Gris, *Europe-Almanach*, pp. 34–35, Potsdam, 1925.

packages, and the mass-produced heroes of the comic strips—are their preferred images. These artists have a just resentment against the gigantic semantic conspiracy of newspapers, billboards, and television to catch public attention through deliberate doubletalk. They recognize how language—verbal and visual—is exploited to force the responses of a passive public. But, parallel with this awareness, they have developed, through familiarity, an attachment to objects that never left their visual field. Their unresolved mixture of personal, hidden loves and critical social commentary forgets the revolutionary achievements of the artists of the last century.

In spite of all the claims and counterclaims, most of the mushrooming art movements have forgotten the essential role of artistic creation. By and large, the art world has become the scene of a popularity contest manipulated by appraisers and impresarios who are blind to the fundamental public role of the artistic image. In inverse proportion to the shrinking public relevance of art, a great deal of public noise is made: grunts and groans, screams and whines periodically sprinkled with sudden and unjustified cries of exuberance. These noises only mask the absence of a deeper vision of reality. The eager prophets of the *dernier cri* are blind to the basic principle that what makes today is not only today. "From the oldest comes the newest," commented Béla Bartók, an authentic spirit of our time. It is not only the last little twig on a tree that produces a new leaf—the oldest roots and the age-old trunk are needed to channel the sap required for life and growth. Continuity and change, old and new together, form the basis for untwisted development and a full life.

One thing is certain. We cannot indulge in self-torture over dire prognoses or beat our breasts over past mistakes. Neither can we live in a make-believe world of visionary extrapolations. We have to accept the condition of our time if we are to reach the real present.

We seem to be in the grip of a tremendous inertial force that rushes us ahead—away from our deepest roots and without allowing us to think of where we are going or to develop the will to check and control our course. We have inherited concepts of order belonging to a smaller, slower scale of existence; these are becoming increasingly useless in the exploded scale of events. We have been accustomed to making ordered relationships by mapping objects and even individuals in their positions relative to one another. Now we are forced to recognize that objects do not have fixed positions, that human relations are among the things in the man-created environment that have direction and velocity. We have learned to recognize that a description of position tells only half the story. A still photo of a heavily trafficked street does not tell us which cars are moving and which are still. Our information must include velocity as well as position if we are to do anything about the situation. Similarly, in the kinetic situation of today, changing social forces in hitherto neglected areas of the world are posing the demand for an understanding of dynamic social processes. Our understanding can be meaningful only if the position, direction, and velocity of the processes are given.

To structure our chaotic physical and social environment as well as our knowledge and values, we have to accept the conditions of the new scale and learn to use the tools that have grown from it. Both the world we create inside our heads and the world we create outside our bodies exist in order to preserve the condition of life. We ourselves and our tremendously extended feelers of sensibilities, tools of observation, structures that shelter us and give us physical comfort, have, ultimately, one objective—

to preserve the condition of life in the internal environment and to preserve it in the fullest human sense, not in the biological sense alone. Our human system, if we may so call it, is a network of interacting variables with the power of purposeful self-regulation.

Artistic sensibility and the imaginative act are key factors in human self-regulation of the interacting variables of our man-shaped inner and outer worlds. Artistic sensibility is seeking new images to give us our bearings. As nineteenth-century creative vision projected the images of health and fullness, light, space, and color, and the inner richness of fully lived life, so twentieth-century artistic sensibility is trying to read the signs between life and no life, between life as it is and life as it could be. It tries to create dynamic images of order that can domesticate the wildly spiraling forces of expansion.

This book, a volume of the *Vision and Value* series, focuses upon such aspects of the environment, but within a framework that includes not only artistic creation but the scientific comprehension of phenomena as well.

The opening section of this volume deals with broad aspects of motion. Of the five essays in this section, one is by a physicist, another by an art historian, two by psychologists, and one by a philosopher. The essays have in common their implicit acceptance of the complementary unities inherent in their respective areas.

The first essay, by Gerald Holton, gives a synoptic view of the historical transformations of our conceptual model of motion, emphasizing the central role of motion in the history of thought. He also touches upon the progressive development of what he calls the "deallegorization" of motion. With clarity and precision, he traces the changes in the interpretation of motion, from early allegorization—personification of hidden movers behind the moving features of the environment—to a complete mathematization in the theories of contemporary physics. The early heroes and anthropomorphic gods—the golden chariot of the sun god Helios, drawn by fire-breathing horses; Hermes with his winged sandals; the winged horse of Pegasus—are distant memories. All are now faded into the imageless, bodyless abstractions of such contemporary physics as quantum mechanics. Contemporary science, as Holton puts it, "progressively unmasked movement and change to find local motion behind them." The infinite variety of possible motion has turned out to be an illusion. The gradual abstraction of the visible, animated world and the restriction of its movement to certain limited processes is by no means the dehumanizing loss that it might appear. The more abstract mathematical thought has become, the greater has been its power to handle the palpable facts of immediate reality. The process of deallegorization and mathematization of our mental models of motion has led to the discovery and control of nuclear energies. Besides, it has led to a living interdependence between the abstract and the concrete, the recognition of which, Holton suggests, has far-reaching creative consequences.

James Ackerman, in the second essay, deals with the nature of art movements and the transformations of artistic idioms. He utilizes the notion of evolution to illuminate the nature of stylistic change in art. Ackerman is fully aware of the dangers implicit in applying one field of human knowledge to another. He recognizes that superficial parallels between entelechy and vitalism in evolutionary theories, including evolutionary theories in art, have led many good men down blind alleys. Some historians of art, smelling danger, have abandoned the use of evolutionary concepts. Today, however, biological evolution has a new, firmer foundation, and historians of art can apply its knowledge with profit. With disciplined but imaginative exploration of concepts such as origin, natural selection, radiation, adaptation, survival of the fittest, and specialization applied to stylistic change, Ackerman comes to some interesting conclusions.

In the history of art, adaptation has a particular, complex, and significant meaning. Adaptation of artistic forms to the environment is a two-way process, for the environment also adapts to man-made forms. The evolutionary history of artistic forms takes place through individual variation without the implication that there is a directing agent or a predetermined goal. There is a complex interaction between the unique contribution of an individual imaginative power and the historic changes in the culture: "While the individual imagination generates change, society, including artists, guides its rate and direction, but only by post facto selectivity; the environment can prompt imaginative solutions by posing challenging problems, but is not itself creative." The implication is that a change for the sake of change is a virtue neither in biological nor in artistic evolution. For the most impressive work of art that has a deep and embracing message will have a survival value beyond the time and place of its origin. Old and new, persistence and change interact in a vital historical dialogue. Only by recognizing the inherent needs of certain historic moments—that is, through adaptation—can change occur. But change also implies constancy, a persistent characteristic fabricating the substance of the future.

The third essay, by Dorfles, touches upon the contemporary panorama of the complex interplay between our knowledge and technology of motion, and our psychological, artistic responses to them. Dorfles indicates some of the significant conceptual, technical, and emotional transformations in our industrial world. He points out that the new kinetic conditions have compelled a re-evaluation of inherited artistic idioms. The new conditions have led to new principles of object shaping. These work upon the environment, steering its forces of transformation. Speed has become basic to our twentieth-century condition. The consequence has been a new form of art in which the dynamic characteristics are central. The new awareness and range of sensibility, on the other hand, has led to intense development of new technical motion-recording and -manipulating devices, such as motion pictures and television. In turn, the technology of motion-recording has introduced new visual experiences of reversible motion, and has thus prepared the perceptual ground for new explorations of reality.

The next two essays, by the psychologists Wallach and Gibson—pioneers in the understanding of the motion factor in our perception of the spatial world—help us to clarify the role of motion in our perception. They have one common factor in their specific ways of interpreting motion perception: both accept motion as fundamental to the human grasp of the stable spatial world. Gibson interprets the perception of the spatial world as controlled by the changes in the textural characteristics of the visible surfaces—a theory that grew out of his studies of depth and distance perception with respect to aviation. He believes that a visual space is not perceived as an object or a set of objects, but rather as a continuous surface or sets of adjoining surfaces; that certain features of the retinal image retain a constant property in the continuous transformation of surfaces. Such invariant properties of the constantly changing retinal image as the upright character of the phenomenal world, and the constancy of shape, color, and size, are the scaffolding of our spatial orientation. Wallach has demonstrated that our perception of spatial depth becomes clear through a sequence of changing stimulations. Together, through their complementary interaction, the stable spatial world and the kinetic changing world shape our picture of our surroundings.

While the essays of the first part of the volume deal with broad, general aspects of motion, subsequent essays deal with the specific character of artistic expressions utilizing motion as their central theme. Some emphasize the rhythmic features of the kinetic experience; others, the contrapuntal or melodic characteristics of the sequence pattern of mobile visual phenomena.

Stanley W. Hayter's essay deals with techniques of projecting an image of movement. He surveys the morphological characteristics of an image of motion: direction, cheirality, velocity, and rhythm. The graphic equivalent of motion is the eye movement of observer and maker. Hayter describes, with an engineer's precision, the various dynamic linear configurations underlying the experience of motion. In his morphological study of motion, he emphasizes the pulsations of rhythmic motion. Here he points out that the devices which some artists are employing are related to mathematical series and progressions. The artist's image of motion has to do with the modification of the field, rather than the action of an object or the displacement of a point. There are new avenues open, and the artist, if he is willing to explore them, may find the means to orchestrate his images into rich, living rhythm.

The next two papers deal again with the new attempts of artists to incorporate mobile experience in creative expression. George Rickey's essay, guided by the eyes of the practicing artist, surveys aspects of physical motion and their possible application in sculpture and painting. Rickey's essay performs the useful task of presenting the total motion vocabulary used today. Careful listing of the growing range of idioms used by artists to explore motion or create virtual or induced motion gives younger artists the vocabulary and grammar with which to express themselves in contemporary motion terms. Rickey emphasizes both the means and the motivating ideas of artists, and ends his essay with the hope that reporting to the coming generation of artists on the means available and the dreams and efforts of the pioneers may help in the realization of a new form of art.

Mrs. Kuh's essay deals with the same artistic efforts but looks at them with the eye of the sympathetic, informed observer. Her report on the current state of kinetic art is made with understanding and with a recognition of the essential frame of reference of artistic values within the broadest context of contemporary life.

The next essay, by the painter Karl Gerstner, is a case study of one kind of contemporary effort to induce motion by the static forms of the painted surface. By rearranging certain constant units, he generates patterns exhibiting symmetrical, rhythmic, and sequential characteristics. By mirroring, permutation, and transposition of the position and tonal values of elements he induces directions of movement: inward or outward spiral; left or right diagonal; and, consequently, a specific rhythmic character to the series of movements. In conclusion, Gerstner reminds us that there are innumerable possibilities for grouping but only a few laws governing chance configurations. We can perceive thousands of different kinds of order, but a hundred thousand kinds of disorder are perceived as one.

The next group of essays is concerned with the structural problems of successive images. Hans Richter, the pioneer film maker, introduces this group. He traces his own creative path from easel painting to motion pictures for the creative tool that best expresses motion—the key concern of twentieth-century man in the visual arts. He recalls how he and Viking Eggeling, as early as the end of World War I, became interested in the problems of movement and time, how they first took musical counterpoint as their starting place and, basing themselves on this, developed a new visual system of dynamic and polar arrangement of opposing visual energies. With passionate involvement, they developed an impressive analysis of contrast and analogy as a key to visual continuity. The Chinese scroll was another form of expression that helped them to develop their understanding of movement as a structuring device. From these early hints, Richter crystallized an understanding of some of the essential aspects of motion pictures as rhythmic, contrapuntal structure. But he did not forget that the nature of form is set by what is formed, that the formal structure of any creative form has to grow from the interplay of all the physiological and psychological involvements of men. The motion picture has to incorporate the total range of human response—conscious and unconscious—but all these aspects have to be structured with a measure of order, a new measure born of ordering movement.

The next essay, by Gessner, investigates the various motions useful in the organization of film space. It is a useful summary of the various devices and possibilities of film language, and can be stimulating in the crystallization of further studies in this direction.

The last two essays explore the new possibilities of contrapuntal organization of visual images. Sequence order, instead of being applied to an almost controlled group of observers, as in a film showing, is projected to two broader open-scale systems of observer involvement.

Washburn discusses the problems of structure and continuity in the presentation of paintings and sculptures on a monumental exhibition scale such as the Carnegie International in Pittsburgh, which he directed. It is a rewarding investigation, for, in its condensed focus, it provides insights into the growth problems of sequence structures, which play an ever more dominant role as the visual environment becomes bigger and more complex.

Appleyard, the city planner, projects the problems of dynamic visual organization on the most challenging scale. No speculation about the visual future is more fascinating than stargazing into the potential aesthetic qualities that may grow out of sequence experience on so tremendous a scale as that of the urban environment. We are all seduced by some aspects of richness in our dynamic setting, but this aspect promises richer visual meaning than any that our visual environment has offered before.

New conditions challenge the idioms of our sensibilities. A new situation compels us to develop new idioms of vision. Today, we face such a revision of the tools of our vision.

There are two basic ways in which the revision of vision may proceed. One is through technical inventions that extend the power and reach of our visual experience. The microscope, the X-ray, the stroboscopic light enable us to see what previously was too small, too large, too dense, too far, or too fast to see; motion pictures, television, and a variety of techniques of transforming signals from one mode to another have extended the range of man-created images. Second, besides these obvious technical achievements, there is another, more subtle means through which our vision is transformed. The complex dynamics of the visual world lead to new habits of seeing, as expressed in some works of contemporary art.

With the help of these extended visual tools and ways of seeing, we may be able to face the second activity fundamental to our individual and social equilibrium. In our social life, the individual's survival and self-realization can be guaranteed only by the cooperative acts of a growing radius of other men. Communication is the joint that makes cooperation possible. Communication, utilized with passion and enlightenment, can clarify the notion of cooperation. For, if we only look, we cannot help but recognize that whatever we require to meet our present physical, emotional, and intellectual needs—a loaf of bread, a book, a film—is, as a physical object, the terminal point of an almost unending chain of cooperative human acts. The book in front of us, its paper, its printer's ink, is the final product of innumerable interlocking human actions, ranging from felling timber in Finland to mining the lead for type metal in Colorado, and so on. Furthermore, the printed words, the thoughts that build the total meaning of the book, are products of imaginative acts of men, ranging back in history and welling up to the present. Thus communication not only made the book a physical reality, but also made the very words and thoughts of the book a symbolic reality. To make this factual cooperation in our physical and intellectual realms a lived, conscious reality, communication has to be used with new understanding and on a scale that has been made possible only today.

The information coming from our individual sensibilities is brought into common knowledge by social communication. As our central nervous system controls the information it receives and transmits its decisions to our limbs and organs, so our social knowledge, amassed through intercommunication, guides our social acts. By crystallizing a common symbolic system, our cultural, social body develops a central control. What we experience will be registered, evaluated, and controlled by the symbolic core of our cultural body. The decisions we make, consciously or unconsciously, and the consequent steps we take in our social and physical environment have to be monitored properly back to a central symbolic system.

One of man's persistent dreams is of a true *universitas*—a living fabric of the best knowledge of a given time. Today, more than ever, we have the opportunity to found such a *universitas*. Our powerful new tools of communication can circulate knowledge on a social scale hitherto undreamed of. Our complex social situation and intricate economic network make the intercommunication of knowledge and feeling a condition of survival. And, in spite of all contrary signs, we have accumulated impressive new insights, both in the impersonal, rational cognition of science and the personal, sensed cognition of our perceptions and feelings in the arts. But all this knowledge of eye, heart, and brain is kept in separate realms. To promote a favorable intellectual climate for an intercommunication that will bring our present knowledge together is a challenging and urgent task.

The series of books to which this volume belongs is an attempt to face this task and feel out possible connecting links among various realms of knowledge. It is inherent in the nature of the task that no attempt is made to force an artificial unity through a disciplined treatment of a coherent theme. The goal is not to blend but to link different imaginative human insights; it is hoped that there will be suggested some common contours in various areas of knowledge. To achieve this outcome it is necessary to forge new tools and develop a methodology suited to the new discipline of intercommunication. Just as the closest-matching contours make the dovetail joint perform its conjunctive role the most effectively, so our new vistas will come together if we find the common boundaries of the two interdependent important ways of responding to the world that we call art and science.

Pitt-Rivers, a great anthropologist of the last century, made the pertinent observation that changes and improvements in tools and ideas arise not only from "far-reaching steps of inventive imagination, but also from long courses of renewed and even accidental alterations." It is hoped, then, that preparing a favorable cultural ground will induce interaction of knowledge on all levels, and thus raise the level of individual and social self-realization. This volume, like the others in the series, offers no sudden major revelations, but suggests some seminal patterns of "interseeing" needed for the living process of growing understanding.

MOTION IMAGES

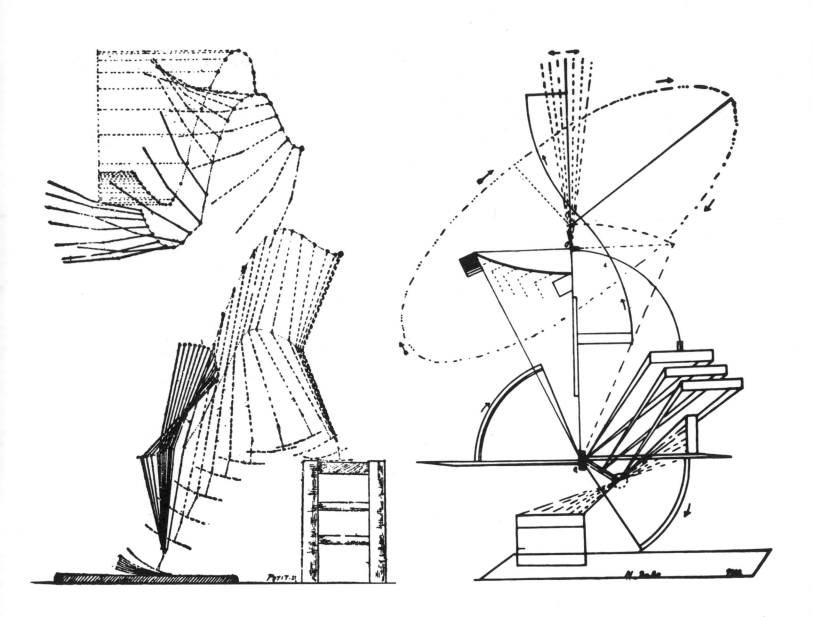

Etienne Jules Marrey. Motion study of human movement.
Reproduced from E. J. Marrey, *Movement*, 1895.

Naum Gabo. Drawing for a kinetic sculpture, 1915.

Stroboscopic motion study.
Photograph by Professor Harold E. Edgerton,
Massachusetts Institute of Technology.

a

b

a: Child's drawing.

b: Pattern made by a moving flashlight in the dark.
Student photograph by D. Monell, 1940,
for the editor's visual design course,
Massachusetts Institute of Technology.

c: Gyorgy Kepes. Drawing, 1939.

c

Jackson Pollock.
Number 14, 1948. Duco on Tempera.
Collection Miss Kay Ordway.

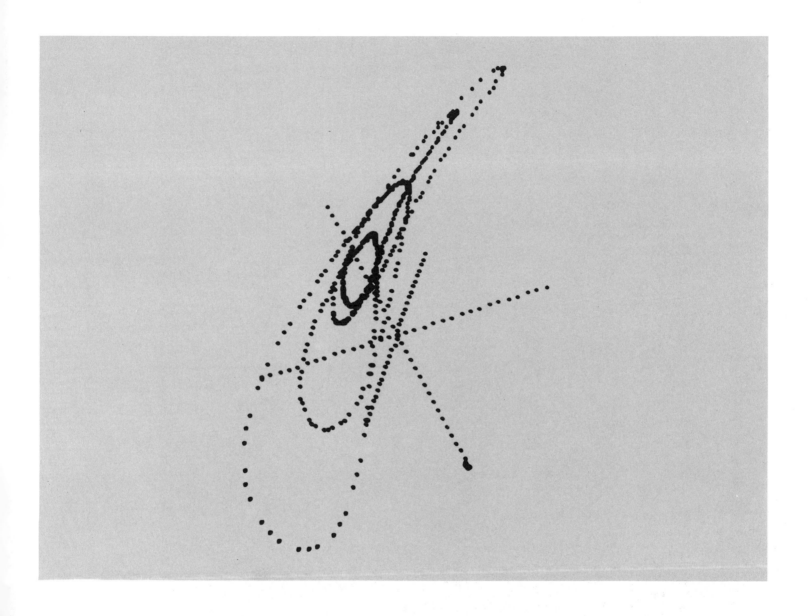

Iterations of non-linear transformations performed by high-speed Los Alamos computers, displayed on the face of an oscilloscope. Study by S. M. Ulam and P. R. Stein, Los Alamos Scientific Laboratory of the University of California, Los Alamos, New Mexico.

Jēkabs Zvilna. Time and Motion Study. The image has been developed by coating a glass sheet with carbon black. Oil has been used to distribute the carbon. The oil in continuous motion has been exposed to gravity.

Electronic track in liquid hydrogen bubble chamber.
Photograph by Alvaroz Group, University of California.

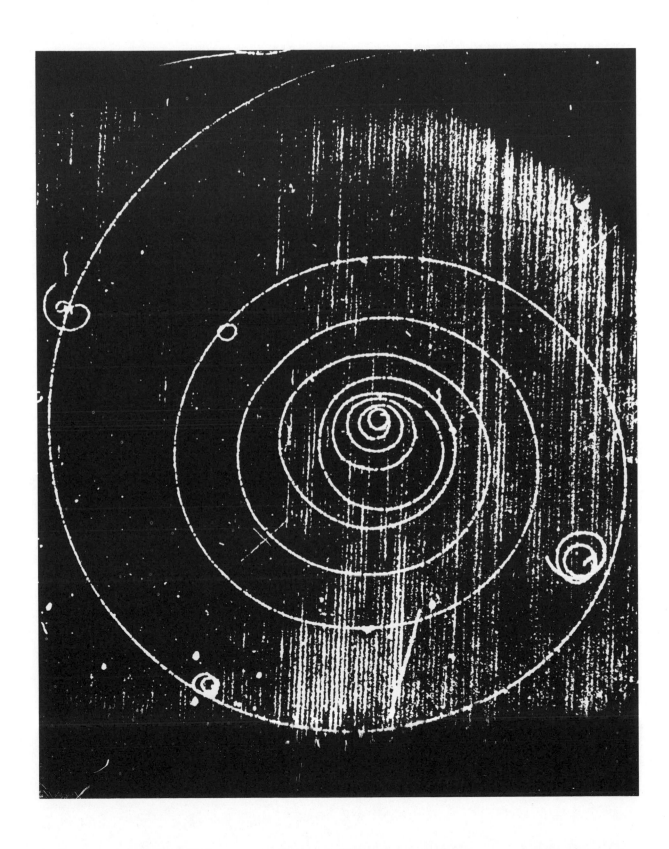

Aerial view of the New York approaches to the George Washington Bridge.
(Photo Courtesy Project Sky Count, The Port of New York Authority)

Robert Delaunay. *Rhythm without End*, 1935. Gouache.
The Museum of Modern Art, New York.

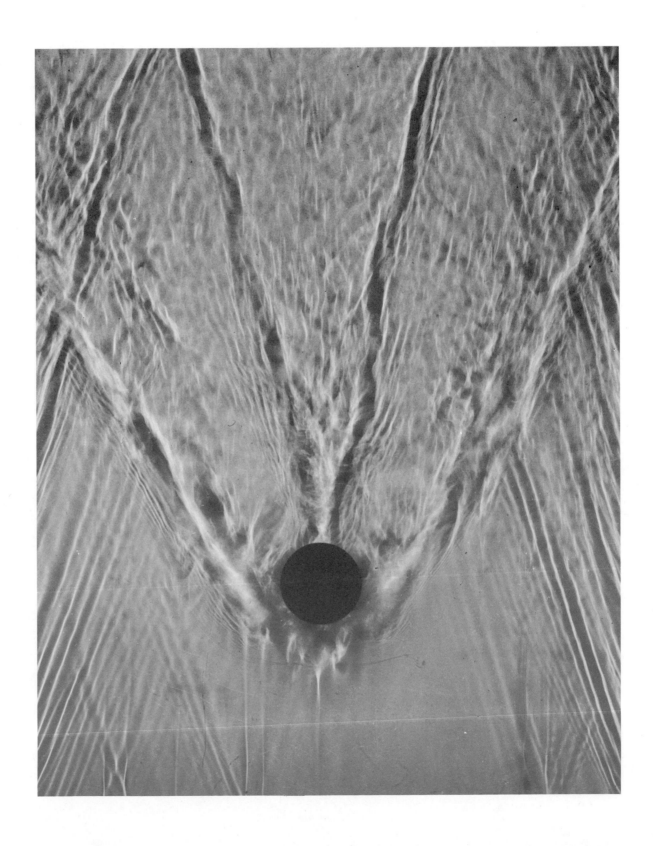

Fluid passing an obstacle.
(*Photo Courtesy General Electric Company*)

a: Aerial photograph of the African coastline.
(*Photo Courtesy Aero Service Corporation*)

b: Kasimir Malevich. *Suprematist Composition:
The Feeling of Motion and Resistance*, 1916.

c: Aerial photograph of an island.
(*Photo Courtesy Lockwood, Kessler and Bartlett*)

a

b

c

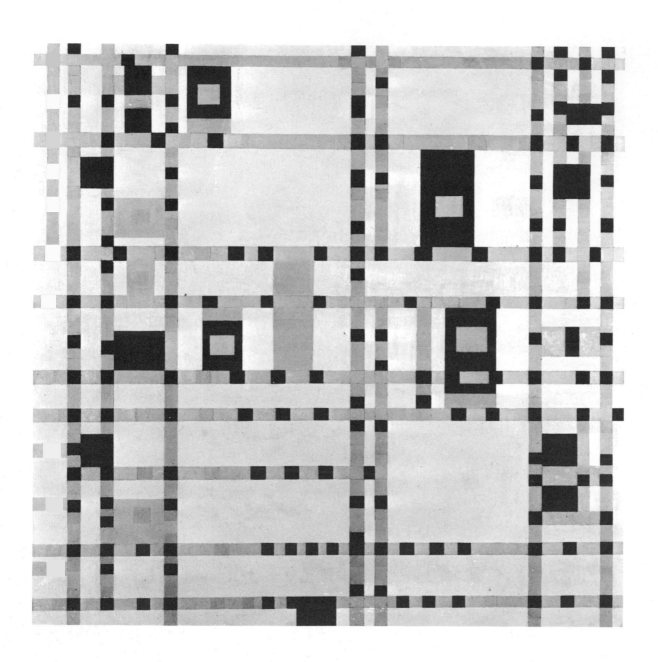

Piet Mondrian.
Broadway Boogie-Woogie, 1942–43.
Museum of Modern Art, New York.

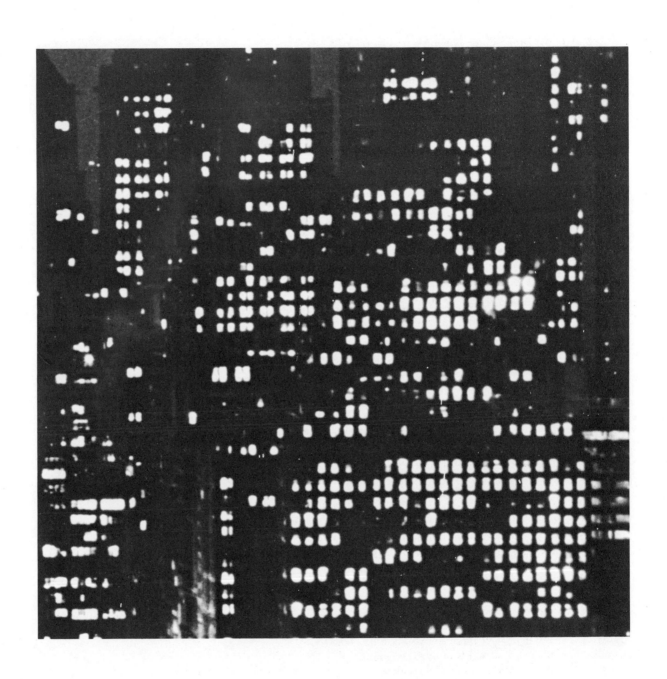

Detail of the New York skyline at night.
(*Photo Courtesy The Port of New York Authority*)

Executed for K.L.M. Office, New York

If we look down from an airplane on a nightscape of a city, an intoxicating new visual wonder is revealed to us. The weary masks of men struggling for identity and survival recede into the distance, and the smoke, the dirt, and the bustle of the streets disappear under a glowing carpet—the illuminated city seen from the air. The shameless sales talks of the neon advertising signs are redrawn, their luminous lines of red and green mingling with the shimmering silver threads of moving car lights and the winking points of traffic signals. All are woven into a common fabric with the sparkling jewels of street lamps, windows, and lights from a hundred different sources.

This new exhilarating perspective is the product of the lucky meeting of two great technical achievements. Artificial illumination, in particular electric light, and advanced techniques of flight, have brought light, color, and space into the common focus of a living mural on a tremendous scale.

"Color," Herman Melville lamented during his trip to England more than a century ago, "is already a little old-fashioned in this drab, utilitarian England. This is the City of Dis: black coats, black hats, have survival value in a sulfur and brimstone world; the damned need protective coloration." If he were alive today to see our own industrial cities, he would utter the same words about America, but even more strongly. For our own cities, when exposed by the daylight, reveal a bleached, ugly, corroded fabric; dirty streets, fake buildings, crudely commercial advertising signs, tangled, stuttering movements of men and machines. But if he could rise high into the air and see the metropolis in its evening raiment —festive, rich, and clean—he would exclaim at this new world of light and color. For the distant view of the city offers a magnificent image that excites our reverence and awe. Here is a new window to the cosmos, a new mirror in which to see ourselves and to envisage our hopes and our potential strength. Here is a garden of delights, a glimpse of a lost Eden of the eye. When the evening comes and the lights turn on, the city is transformed, however chaotic, blighted, and ugly its daytime face. Points, lines, plane figures, and volumes of light, steady and winking, moving and still, white and colored, from windows, signs, spectaculars, headlights, traffic lights, and street lights—all these compose a fluid, luminous wonder, one of the grand sights of our age. Though this impressive display is produced almost by accident, a by-product of utility, its magnificence reminds us of the glory of the great stained-glass windows of thirteenth-century cathedrals. This accidental splendor contains the promise of a new art in the orchestration of light on either a vast or limited scale.

Eisenstein, the pioneer film director, gave a convincing verbal image of this new sense of *luminous space.* "All sense of perspective and realistic depth is washed away by a nocturnal sea of electric advertising. Far and near, small and

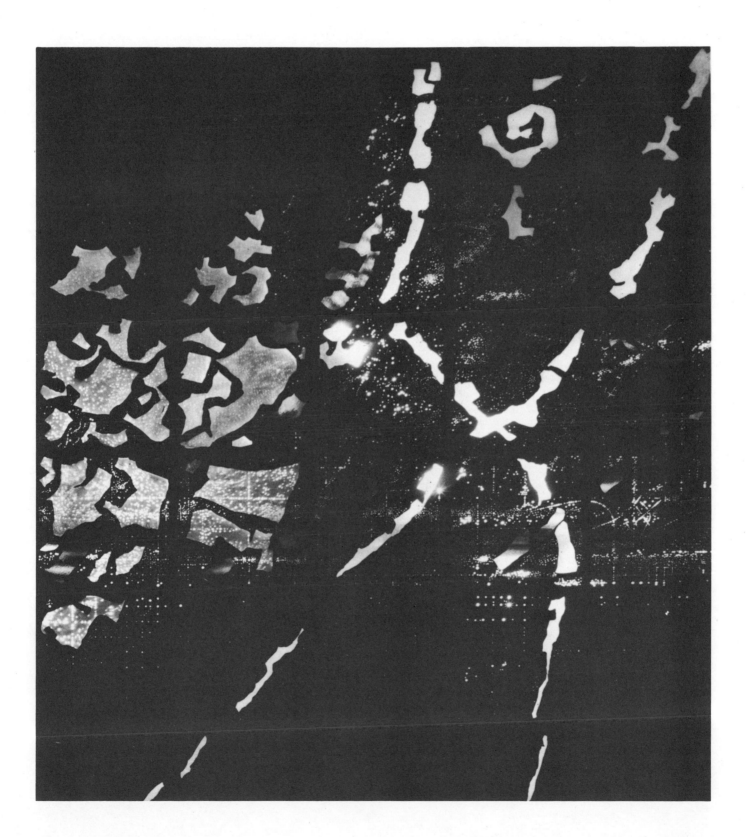

large, soaring aloft and dying away, racing and circling, bursting and vanishing—these lights tend to abolish all sense of real space, finally melting into a single plane of colored light points and neon lines moving over a surface of black-velvet sky. It was thus that people used to picture stars—as glittering nails hammered into the sky. Headlights on speeding cars, highlights on receding rails, shimmering reflections on the wet pavements—all mirrored in puddles that destroy our sense of direction (which is top? which is bottom?), supplementing the mirage above with a mirage beneath us, and rushing between these two worlds of electric signs—we see them no longer on a single plane, but as a system of theater wings, suspended in the air, through which the night flood of traffic lights is streaming."

Antoine de Saint-Exupéry, explorer of the beauty of aerial vision, a true adventurer in vistas unchained from bonds to the earth, sensed the liberated vision inherent in these new aerial experiences. "Horizon? There was no longer a horizon. I was in the wings of a theater cluttered up with bits of scenery. Vertical, oblique, horizontal, all of plane geometry was awhirl. A hundred transversal valleys were muddled in a jumble of perspectives. . . . For a single second, in a waltzing landscape like this, the flyer has been unable to distinguish between vertical mountain sides and horizontal planes . . ."

Artists a generation before us recognized the need for a new frame of reference for their creative vision. They were dreaming of new creative ways to project their responses to the new vistas. Painters, photographers, and film makers had been struggling to find valid new idioms with which to bring space and light into a living focus. Magnificent artistic statements were made with pigments on canvas or recorded with light on photosensitive film. Nevertheless, artists were frustrated and tantalized because the limits of their media narrowed and condensed the explosive range of the new experiences. Needed were a new scale of tools and a new scale of setting. Only by accepting light as autonomous, as plastic luminosity that can be molded, shaped, and formed with the same limitless plasticity as the clay in which sculptors model, could the artist hope to find a valid correspondence between his new scale of experience and his artistic expression of it. And only a spatial surrounding that is generous enough in scale to shelter the explosive luminous tools could provide an adequate background. The isolated, sheltered, small space of a room at home or in a museum is suffocatingly narrow for the fluid power of light in action. The new, rich intensities of artificial light sources, if used creatively, must be woven into the bigger fabric of the night cityscape. The mirroring of the shop windows and the interpenetration of mobile vistas, with their continuous transformations of space and form, must be accepted as a background to a creative figure shaped by the moving contours of actual lights.

An opportunity to try out the new tools in their new setting was given to me by a commission for a mural in the offices of a leading airline in the heart of New York City. The theme was the richness of the aerial vista of the nocturnal city. The tool chosen was light in action. The mural, over fifty feet long and eighteen feet high, is a gray aluminum screen with some sixty thousand random perforations and larger cut-outs. The sources of light are a multitude of incandescent, fluorescent, and spot-light bulbs and tubes behind the mural surface, controlled by timing and switching devices that actuate the circuits. The purpose was to create, with all these intricate devices, a fluid, luminous pattern with random changes, alive through their continuous transformation of color intensity, direction, and pattern. To avoid the mechanical repetition inherent in a mechanized device, many thousand different color filters were placed behind the perforations in random distribution.

The underlying design thought in this mural was based upon a principle used in Peruvian fabrics: maintaining a rhythmic interplay between a constant pattern and a changing pattern. On the one hand, on the permanent pattern of the perforation a shifting color scheme was superimposed, and, on the other hand, on the recurring time pattern of brightness there were superimposed cut-outs and perforations varying greatly in shape and linear direction.

Though the mural has a defined architectonic role in the design of the office, which is on the street level, I intended beyond this to make it a part of the large space of the street outside, sometimes blending and sometimes competing with the rivers of light generated by moving automobiles, giving and taking light from the surroundings, both invading the outside space and being invaded by it.

GERALD HOLTON

SCIENCE
AND
THE DEALLEGORIZATION OF MOTION

In his influential book, *The Origins of Modern Science, 1300–1800,* Herbert Butterfield indicated the role which our topic, Motion, has played in the history of thought: "Of all the intellectual hurdles which the human mind has been faced with and has overcome in the last fifteen hundred years, the one which seems to me to have been the most amazing in character and the most stupendous in the scope of its consequences is the one relating to the problem of motion. . . ."

Herbert Butterfield does not use superlatives lightly, and yet he seems to me to have underestimated the matter on three counts. First, the problems of motion in science and philosophy has an even longer history. The scholastic adage *ignorato motu ignoratur natura* (who knows not motion, knows not nature) had earlier been also a leitmotif, in its changing contexts, in Eleatic, Atomistic, Platonic, and Aristotelian writings. In the last, particularly, we can still see the concept of motion in a rich, primal context, one in which movement as we now understand it plays a subordinate role. Aristotle's definition of motion preserves a generality which we can reconstruct only with great effort: *Motus est actus entis in potentia secundum quod in potentia est* (motion is the actuality of that which *is* potentially, viewed from the standpoint of potential being). Here motion denotes any transition from potentiality to actuality, whether this change be generation or corruption of a substantial form, whether it be alteration in quality or in quantity, or whether it refers to occupation of a different place (local motion in the narrow sense).

This view, as E. J. Dijksterhuis has correctly said in *The Mechanization of the World Picture,* introduces emphatically the proposition "that the subject matter of science is change"; but this view also emphatically denies that the study of change is *solely* the prerogative of science. Aristotle's concept of motion is, I would suggest, a great allegory, in which local motion is only one of many attributes.

As it has turned out, local motion took on a predominant position in science because to some extent the other kinds of motion could be reduced to it. For example, qualitative change in physics or chemistry or biology—whether it is a change of phase from gas to liquid or solid, or a change from one chemical substance to another, or the development of organization in a cell, or the decay of an elementary particle into different products—is understood by first invoking the relative motion of constituent parts. In the Aristotelian context, this would not be the centrally important aspect of qualitative change. In the context of present knowledge, the motion of particles and the propagation of energy (e.g., in fields) are central tools of explanation. Science has progressively unmasked movement and change to find local motion behind them.

Moreover, the unmasking continues to our day. In addition to its greater antiquity, the problem of motion has had a longer life than Butterfield seems to be ready to grant. The problem of motion was not settled by Galileo and Newton, but seems to confront us in science anew with every great advance. It was in this century that Einstein showed the speed of light to be the maximum speed in free space for any physical object. Beyond that speed, all others are inherently impossible. Niels Bohr then showed that periodic motions are quantized. That is, an electron cannot orbit at any arbitrary distance from the nucleus, but is constrained to certain "allowed" orbits whose radii are related to one another as the ratios of whole numbers (such as $1 : 4 : 9 \ldots$).

Then quantum mechanics of the 1920's brought out the statistical nature of the motion of subatomic particles and of light energy. No longer can one think of the point-by-point progress of an electron in its orbit, or of a photon passing through an opening in an opaque obstacle and going on in a straight line to a screen beyond it. Given the state of motion of electrons or photons in their specified environment at one instant, one can assign the *probability* of having electrons or photons materialize or register at another location and at a later instant.

The simultaneous determination of the position and the velocity of a moving particle had always been tacitly considered to be possible with arbitrary precision; but now such measurement was revealed to be afflicted with an inherent, coupled indeterminacy. As one attempts to make one of these more precise, the other necessarily becomes less precise. And recently, yet another restriction on conceivable motions appeared which rocked physics to its very foundations. In the radioactive decay of some nuclei, it was shown that the motion of the emitted β-ray is not equally probable in both the up and down directions, for example, but that instead one direction is preferred.

On the human scale of motion, the Galileo-Newton discussion still suffices. But on the atomic and subatomic levels—the levels on which large-scale behavior finds its explanation in scientific terms—the history of recent science has been a history of accumulating restrictions with respect to motion. An infinite variety of motions which are imaginable, and therefore may have been thought to be possible, have turned out to be impossible. In every other respect we have seen a proliferation—of types of forces, of kinds of particles—but with respect to motion there has been a reduction, a structuring, a progressive taming. With each step, the Aristotelian allegory of motion as all-pervading, undelineated change has been more and more abandoned.

There is another sense in which Butterfield's remark on motion is too restrictive. It is the implication (which may not have been intended) that the problem of motion is to be dealt with mainly by the scientist. The other essays in the present volume attest to the fact that the problem of motion is as central and variegated in art as it is in science. More to the point for the purpose of this essay is the fact that the influence of the arts on scientific sensibilities, while not as easy to exhibit by example as is the influence in the reverse direction, is just as real. Erwin Panofsky's classic study, *Galileo as a Critic of the Arts*, made this case as beautifully as it will ever need to be made.

It will be recalled that Panofsky asked why Galileo had failed to use or even refer to Kepler's laws of planetary motion in his long and strenuous fight on behalf of the Copernican system of planetary astronomy. This failure, which hobbled Galileo's case severely by our present standards, had always deeply puzzled historians of science, for Kepler's contribution was then (and is still) by far the most natural and convincing door to Copernicanism. Galileo's insistence on superposed circular motions was both more clumsy and less accurate. Panofsky proved that Galileo's decision rested on aesthetic grounds. He could not bring himself to accept Kepler's elliptical planetary orbits, for the ellipse, the wretchedly distorted version of the godlike circle, was the very signature of the Mannerist and anticlassical style of art that Galileo so despised.

It would seem from this example that the effects of the arts on science may not be salutary. If Galileo had not been so well trained and genuinely involved in the visual arts, he might have been able to make a better case for heliocentric astronomy. But the curious thing is that ultimately he was right.

The analysis of planetary motion on elliptical orbits is repugnant not only to classicistic aesthetics, but also to the uncivilized hand calculator and the impartial computing machine. Periodic motions are dealt with most simply by regarding them as the sum and total result of a suitable number of superposed circular (harmonic) motions of different amplitude, frequency, and phase. In the end, we now use Kepler's diagrams to imagine planetary motion, but we adopt Galileo's commitment to the circle to understand the motion computationally.

It seems to me that this case illustrates a general principle. When a creative person in one field responds to another field—a Galileo transfering aesthetic criteria from the arts to astronomical work, or conversely, a Juan Gris discovering in Relativity Theory directives for painting—the result *on the surface of it* is apt to be disappointing. Even within a given field, be it physics or painting, analogy is more often dangerous than fruitful; and between unlike fields the transfers that invite themselves are often so superficial that they amount to little more than puns. But this need not be true on another level of transfer—a level whose existence may be proved only in the light of later advances, but which had been accessible to the perception of the genial creator. Thus it was nearly 200 years after Galileo's decision to stick to circles that Fourier discovered the fact that any function of a variable can be expanded in a series of sines of multiples of the variable, thereby enabling us to subject Keplerian motion to Galilean analysis.

I do not wish to propose a concrete mechanism of prescience to explain the ultimate rightness of Galileo's decision (though it be "rightness" in a sense quite different from that which he could have specifically known). Rather, I am proposing that we deal with these matters by considering that such men, while forced to phrase their criteria and decisions in a language appropriate to the contemporary state of knowledge (including their own), may nevertheless also understand the problems they are wrestling with in a more general context—possibly on a nonverbal level, as Einstein suggested in Jacques Hadamard's *The Psychology of Invention in the Mathematical Field.* Pretelescopic observational astronomy, seventeenth-century aesthetic theory, and harmonic analysis appear to be, if one examines the textbooks in these fields, separate and unrelated fields of study. What the delayed triumph of Galileo illustrates, however, is that we may also consider them to be different specialized views of a more general allegory, one of which a Galileo sees more than he can readily describe.

Let me illustrate the same proposition by another example. Just as some of the arts have felt the shaping influence of the sciences, so has also the study of history. Henry Adams believed with particularly eloquent faith that the study of history could base itself on such seminal scientific findings as the Second Law of Thermodynamics. In 1909, in the essay "The Rule of Phase Applied to History", he had come to the conclusion (on the basis of an analogy between the course of history and the mechanism for changes of phase in physical systems) that "the future of thought, and therefore of history, lies in the hands of the physicists, and that the future historian must seek his education in the world of mathematical physics." And in his "Letter to American Teachers of History", written in 1910, Henry Adams went on to consider in detail the implication for history and its teaching of the "approaching demise of the solar system", announced by then current astronomy and physics. For the only mechanism that was then known for explaining the continuous emission of light and warmth from our sun was a presumed gradual shrinking of the sun's radius, with an accompanying conversion of its gravitational energy into radiation. The energy so liberated would, by the Second Law, soon be dissipated into useless form. It was therefore "the ultimate destiny of the celestial universe to become atomic dust at $-270°$ centigrade." There is no escape; "the law of Entropy imposes a servitude on all energies, including the mental. The degree of freedom steadily and rapidly diminishes. Without rest, the physicists gently push history down the decline . . . The universe has been terribly narrowed by thermodynamics."

Henry Adams, one could now say, was naïve and wrong. Or at least the teachings of physics at that time were naïve and wrong. For it turns out that the sun does not provide us with energy by constantly shrinking; that would indeed have sufficed for only a relatively short time. Thermodynamics is not predicting an early running-down; the degradationists cannot use that tool now so effectively against the evolutionists. The progress of nuclear physics has taught us that there is a very different and more long-lived mechanism to which the sun owes its ability to radiate energy.

That mechanism is, of course, the thermo-nuclear reaction—the same general process which is responsible for the release of energy in H-bombs. And now we see suddenly that Henry Adams' thermodynamic analogy may have been as unserviceable as was Galileo's fascination with circular motions, but that nevertheless Adams' conclusion, like Galileo's, has later, on different grounds, become all too believable. Galileo could not have known of Fourier, and Henry Adams could not have known of Los Alamos and the Livermore Laboratories. But Galileo had seen the Allegory of Motion, and Adams had seen the Allegory of the new Apocalypse—history being pushed down the decline as the consequence of the release of physical energy and the servitude of "mental energy".

I do not want to throw doubt on the possibility of *direct* routes of valid transfer from science to art or to history or to any humanistic study. Conversely, the route from humanistic study to scientific inspiration *can* on occasion also be valid and direct. Thus Einstein once said that he was able to develop the basic conceptions of the relativity theory on the basis of his study of Hume and Kant; Niels Bohr reported that the Complementarity Principle occurred to him as a result of a philosophical analysis into the contradictory demands of love and justice; and Sigmund Freud, in the very first letter in the new collection by Ernst L. Freud, wrote to Emil Fluss (16 June 1873), describing one particularly successful—and significant—part of the general examination (*Matura*) he had just passed before entering the university: "The Greek essay succeeded better, 'praiseworthy,' the only one—a thirty-three-verse passage from King Oedipus; I had read this passage also on my own and made no secret of it."[1]

And yet, more important than the direct connections that may be occasionally surmised are the indirect connections, *the sharing of a common allegory*. The practicing artist who is intrigued with science may conceivably find something directly meaningful in the study of the working physicists' differential equations governing the motion of larger bodies, or the operator relations governing the behavior of electrons. But it seems to me much more important that he should understand that these equations are painfully wrought attempts to fashion out of the general concept of motion a limited concept that accentuates some features of it and suppresses others. By paying close attention to vestigial clues, and even better by studying the history of the formation of scientific concepts, he will discover those places where scientific study is (or used to be) connected to the same general allegory which nourishes the artist's own specialized conceptions.

He may also discover closely related difficulties plaguing science and art. For example, differential equations, the usual tool for describing motion in physics, accentuate continuity and are generally helpless in the fact of discontinuity. Yet measurement, the process which gives meaning to the equations, is inherently a discontinuity-producing process. On the subatomic level, the measurement of the velocity of an object changes its velocity. On the scale of larger objects, the measurement of their speed generally necessitates doing something equivalent to taking snapshots, frozen, cartoon-strip slices of experience framed in hard, black outlines against the flowing background of continuing action.

The representation of motion in its full allegorical sense is therefore as impossible in science as it is in painting, or, for that matter, in a literary work. The need to use civilized mathematical functions is incongruous with respect to the discontinuous nature of self-conscious experience; and conversely, the need to take data during experimentation is incongruous with respect to the continuous nature of the processes which are being investigated. Such difficulties are, of course, now of no interest or concern to most scientists. Science may be defined as the study of areas in which such questions have become meaningless. Nevertheless, they are the navel-like scars that show where modern science had to separate itself from earlier natural philosophy.

This process of separation from the generalized meaning of motion during the rise of modern scientific conceptions can be spoken of as a *deallegorization of motion*. The most recent stage has been mentioned earlier: the discovery that whole ranges of thinkable motions are physically impossible or improbable. Before that, in inverse order came the relativization of motion, the introduction of virtual motions into science, and, in the period from the thirteenth to the seventeenth century, the quantification of motion.

Each of these stages represented a stripping away of anthropomorphic and other subjective associations from the definition of motion. But the last-mentioned was the major turning point, not only for the definition of motion, but for the discovery of the very possibility of science as we now understand it. Hence, it is a particularly significant development for study if one wishes to retrace the steps to the common allegory.

Until Newton's time the question of *causation* of motion (dynamics) had two answers. On the one hand, bodies were thought to be subject to propulsion by virtue of some inherent or innate property, be it the attribute of gravity owing to the preponderance of Earth essence, or the action of an *anima* or *virtus*, or of an impetus, or (as still in Newton) a *vis* residing in the moving object. On the other hand, bodies were thought to be also subject to externally caused influences, whether these be the hierarchical structure of the cosmos which guided the body to its proper level, or the tangential pressure and lateral attraction exerted by a line of force that emanates from another object, or the action of the surrounding medium, including external particles during collision (as in the chance collisions of atoms in Democritus, or the vortices of Descartes), or other influences propagated through an ether, a field, or at a distance.

Before these dynamical conceptions of motion as responses to internal or external afflictions could give way to the modern conception of motion as a *relationship of coupled objects,* two developments had to take place in kinematics. The description of motion (without regard to what may have caused it) was shown first to be expressible in terms of geometrical figures, and then in terms of numerical statements. As A. C. Crombie has shown in *Robert Grosseteste and the Origins of Experimental Science,*[2] in the first half of the fourteenth century two methods were in use for expressing functional relationships, one the "word-algebra" of Thomas Bradwardine in Oxford, the other the use of graphs identified with Nicole Oresme at Paris. "These fourteenth-century writers were still primarily concerned with the question how, in principle, to express change of any kind, whether in quantity or in quality, in terms of mathematics, and any treatment they gave of particular optical or dynamical problems was in most cases simply to illustrate a point of method. Yet they succeeded in taking the first steps toward the creation out of the statically conceived Greek mathematics [where the prototype problems were Euclid's propositions and Archimedes' lever in a state of equilibrium] of the algebra and geometry of change that were to transform science in the seventeenth century."[3]

Tentatively and innocently, the mathematization of the allegory of motion had begun. Oresme drew figures, e.g., triangles and even three-dimensional objects, to represent the "quantity of a quality" (e.g., how much speed a body has) with the horizontal dimension standing for *extensio,* the height indicating *intensio.*[4] This was not yet a graph. The interest was in the whole figure, which was to reveal the "properties intrinsic to the quality" depicted.

One result, presented by Oresme in *De Configuratione Qualitate,* became particularly important. It was a geometric proof of a proposition earlier deduced on other grounds at Merton College sometime before 1335. This was the rule that "a uniformly accelerated or retarded movement is equivalent, so far as the space traversed in a given time is concerned, to a uniform movement of which the velocity is equal throughout to the instantaneous velocity possessed by the uniformly accelerated or retarded movement at the middle instant of time."[5]

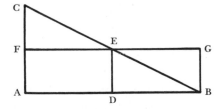

The proof for this depends on the fact that (1) if a uniformly changing quality such as decreasing speed may be represented by a triangle ABC, and (2) if a rectangle ABGF, representing a constant motion, is drawn so that its height AF or BG is just half as large as the long vertical side AC of the triangle, then (3) the area of the triangle and that of the rectangle—representing in each case the total effect of the motion, e.g., the displacement achieved—by simple geometry are equal for both. By inspection it is evident, however, that if DE represents in any way the "degree of intensity" of the changing motion at its midpoint, then one may see that this should be the magnitude of the constant motion which in the end will achieve the same result as the changing motion. In more modern form —now considered essentially as a graph of speed versus time—these triangular and rectangular figures come to the surface again in Galileo's *Discourses on Two New Sciences*. The Mean Speed Rule is an essential part of his discussion of uniformly accelerated motion, the foundation of his whole kinematics, and hence of the proof of his Neoplatonic epistemology.

For as Alexandre Koyré has said,[6] Galileo's work was an experimental proof of Platonism as a methodology of science. The scholastics had always been able to point to the two main failures of Platonism: there was no good theory of terrestrial motion—even Archimedes, the greatest Platonist of antiquity, had only given a science of statics—and there was no successful mathematization of *quality*. Now, in his work on the mechanics of falling bodies, Galileo had met both challenges.

As to the first of these: in the Third Day of Galileo's *Discourses* of 1638, Theorem I, Proposition I is in fact the Mean Speed Rule—replete with essentially the same diagrammatic proof as Oresme's of three centuries before—and with its aid, Galileo draws the famous, ecstatic conclusion, "So far as I know, no one has yet pointed out that the distances traversed, during equal intervals of time, by a body falling from rest, stand to one another in the same ratio as the odd numbers beginning with unity."

We now would put it in the equivalent form that the distance covered in free fall is proportional to the square of the elapsed time. But Galileo had his eye on *numbers, 1, 3, 5, 7 . . .* Geometrical figure and number: these are the language of nature, as the Neoplatonists had always hoped to show. Here at last, in the problem of falling motion, was the proof that triangles and other geometrical figures, and single whole numbers, are indeed the signs in which the Book of Nature has been written. As Koyré said, "La decouverte galiléenne transforme l'échec du platonisme en victoire. Sa science est une revanche de Platon."[7]

What of the second challenge? The mathematization of quality had proved possible for such qualities as motion and size, but not for others such as taste, the sensation of heat, color (though most of these subsequently were indeed also found to have quantifiable aspects). Galileo's decision was simple: to banish the unquantifiable qualities from science—or more properly, to withdraw the attention of science from the realm of unquantifiables. As he wrote in *Il Saggiatore*, "I think that these tastes, odors, colors, etc., on the side of the object in which they seem to exist, are nothing else than mere names, [and] hold their residence solely in the sensitive body; so that if the animal were removed, every such quality would be abolished and annihilated. Nevertheless, as soon as we have imposed names on them, particular and different from those of the other primary and real accidents, we induce ourselves to believe that they also exist just as truly and really as the latter."

The division of concepts according to primary (quantifiable) and secondary qualities, and the abandonment by science of the latter, was, of course, a crucial reduction of the allegory of motion from its original sense of change and movement of every kind. It has frequently been observed that this division, and the consequent mathematical interpretation of nature, has had incalculable consequences on modern thought. This was, E. A. Burtt[8] said, "the first stage in the reading of man quite out of the real and primary realm. . . . Man begins to appear for the first time in the history of thought as an irrelevant spectator and insignificant effect of the great mathematical system which is the substance of reality."

It was unavoidable that we should finally come to this issue, which lies at the bottom of most discussions on the relation between art and science. I have elsewhere argued at length that the implication in statements such as that cited above is unwarranted and erroneous.[9] Far from making man an irrelevant spectator, the insights granted to those who take the trouble to learn the language of science have demonstrated a previously unsuspected capacity of man's mind. The de-emphasis of secondary qualities in science was not a wanton act of dehumanization but rather a strategic decision to reach a worthy human goal, that of understanding nature (including, ultimately, man's nature) in a new way.

The difficulty has perhaps been not that this new way was too hard, but that it turned out to be all too easy. Once the scientists of the seventeenth century had found the key to this particular gate, the road that opened beyond led more and more speedily and deeply into remote and fascinating territory, further and further from the original ground of understanding the world in terms of multiform, undifferentiated, precisionless allegories.

One cannot help regarding this as important progress; and one also cannot help noticing the loss. Only a few at any time seem to be able to move with some assurance on either side of the gate. Galileo himself, of whose aesthetic criteria for planetary orbits we spoke earlier, was an example; there are not many others. The rest of us are far down on some road to deallegorization—each on his own. For just as there are other primal allegories than that of motion (for example, those of space, time, matter, organism, life, death) from which science has progressively moved, so also are there in each case other roads than those of science, leading away from the primal allegories. Perhaps I may be allowed to suggest, *enfin*, that even art, and particularly art, has in this respect suffered the same fate as science. And the treatment of motion in modern visual art may well prove the point. To my eye, at any rate, the distance between primal motion as expressed in ritual dancing or Navaho sandpainting on the one hand, and motion expressed in cinematography, mobiles, and action painting on the other, is as large as the distance between primal motion in Greek nature-philosophy and motion as indicated on a tachometer or an oscilloscope screen. For the process of deallegorization, of reducing, transforming, and abstracting the allegory, is the earmark, not just of science, but of our whole developing culture.

1. Sigmund Freud, *Briefe 1873–1939*, S. Fischer Verlag, Frankfurt am Main (1960), p. 6.

2. Oxford (1953).

3. *Ibid.*, p. 178.

4. See also A. C. Crombie, *Medieval and Early Modern Science*, Doubleday, New York (1959), Vol. II, Chapter I.

5. *Ibid.*, p. 93.

6. See particularly his *Etudes Galiléenes*, Paris (1939), Vols. II and III.

7. *Ibid.*, Vol. III, p. 280.

8. E. A. Burtt,
The Metaphysical Foundations of Modern Science,
Doubleday, New York
(second edition, 1932; 1955 reprint), pp. 89–90.

9. E.g. "Modern Science and the Intellectual Tradition," in G. B. deHuszar (Ed.), *The Intellectuals,* The Free Press of Glencoe, Illinois (1940), and in *Science* (Vol. 131: 1960), pp. 1187–1193.

Art changes from era to era; some styles vanish quickly, others survive and evolve, still others spring up in place of the old and in different parts of the world. About seventy-five years ago, historians, noticing a parallel to biological evolution, picked up some Darwinian metaphors to support a theory of history, but the fact that they misinterpreted Darwin—as did so many of Darwin's successors, even in biology—as giving support to an ineluctable sequence of events directed by some internal or external destiny, ultimately discredited the very thought of collaboration between historical and scientific thought on the nature of change. So when I became interested in the implications of historical theory for criticism, it was as an opponent of "evolutionism", and I realized only later that it was not the use but the misuse of evolutionary concepts that caused the misunderstanding. Historians had cut off contact with biologists just during the period when the latter were cleansing their own stables of finalism and vitalism and were producing a view of life capable of stimulating fresh approaches to cultural history.[1]

The fact that the nineteenth-century historians fell into a trap when they adopted the evolutionary metaphor does not mean that their attempt was misplaced or doomed from the start; the fundamental hypotheses about evolution are *historical* and it would be presumptuous of us to assume that there was nothing to learn about history from the students of life on earth. Though there are radical differences in the data of natural history and of cultural history, their operational hypotheses are formulated in similar ways.[2] The data collected by scientists and historians are merely raw materials to be arranged into rational structures according to hypotheses and principles that are not empirically discovered but created. Since these creations crystallize and represent the point of view of the moment in which they are made, we can expect to discover in them a bridge between the humanities and sciences at any given time. At this generalizing level, technical barriers to understanding—the professional jargon and the mystifying formulas—fall into the background.

Similarities and Contrasts of Method. When we speak of change or evolution in the visual arts we are not thinking about single works, which are mostly inorganic physical objects altered only by damage or de-composition, but of patterns observed in collections of such objects arranged in a linear—usually a chronological—order. In this case, like biologists, we are not observing primarily individual things but trends that can be deduced by comparing them. Comparison is the fundamental method of both fields. The technique is viable only when a number of such things are sufficiently alike to make comparison meaningful, yet sufficiently different that change is apparent. In evolutionary theory, the class of like things is called a taxon (species, genus, family, etc.); in art history, it is called a style.

Both taxa and styles are organized according to a hierarchic, pyramidal classification. As a species (Lion) is a class of a genus (cats with retractible claws), which is in turn in a class of a family (cats) and so on up to a phylum (Vertebrates), so the style of an artist (Botticelli) is classed as belonging to a local period style (Renaissance, early, Florentine), which is part of the Renaissance, Italian, and so on up to the whole span of Western art. Because the really crucial problems of evolution in biology and in art occur at the lower levels of the hierarchy, I am going to compare styles (at the level of the individual and the period) to species rather than to taxa from this point on.

The borderlines between one species and another and one style and another are not always apparent. They may be recognized initially by likenesses and differences in physical characteristics, but the biologist has a more precise basis for classification. Species are interbreeding groups defined by genetic relationship, whereas styles, like other manifestations of culture, cross promiscuously with other styles—even extinct ones. Tortoises always descend from tortoises, but a modern English sculpture may "descend" from a modern French, ancient Roman, or Gothic one, or from all three. So biology differs from history in that its categories are internally organized, and would be so even if there were no biologists (we can make tortoises race, but not mate, with hares), while historical categories like style have to be invented by historians. This is one reason why biological classifications are more descriptive in character (Vertebrates, Amphibia), than historical ones, which show their creators' bias toward a particular interpretation of history and usually are either denigrating (Middle Ages, Gothic, Baroque) or approving (Renaissance, Risorgimento, Enlightenment). Yet the biologist also is influenced by his interpretation of history; thus not all of his Amphibia are amphibious, and not all amphibious animals are Amphibia.

As evolutionists employ fossil evidence to construct an image of change in the past, so art historians examine the products of extinct styles. The historical evidence is much richer, but this advantage obscures the fact that our links can be missing, too. Whole phyla of art are lost, such as Classic Greek wall painting, a major art of antiquity, or the mass of medieval and Renaissance gold- and silversmithery, too precious to survive the poverty and cupidity of later times. The fate of the former affected the entire evolution of later western art, since adherents of the recurrent revivals of antiquity, including painters, saw the Greeks primarily as sculptors; the greatest revival of all—the Renaissance—was well on its way before any Roman painting was known. The losses are due mostly to chance and indifference, not wilful destruction; our ancestors generally kept even what they disliked, and any visitor to provincial American museums will find that bad art has survived as well as good.

But it is the character, not the quantity, of the evidence from the past that makes the fundamental contrast in the nature of the evidence; while the Gothic style as such is as extinct as the Brontosaurus, every surviving, well preserved example of that style can be as lively today as it was when it was made, and as capable of fertilizing fresh creative acts.[3] Indeed, it often happens that products of an extinct style are more influential in the origin of new forms than those of a living style: in the early twentieth century ancient primitive art was more effective than Impressionism.

The Origin of Styles. The origins of art are as little known as the origins of life; in nearly every place where art has appeared, it precedes other records. It must have originated independently in several parts of the world and at intervals of many thousands of years, and wherever it occurred, it survived and propagated. Rarely has an art been extinguished except by force or by the substitution of another art more congenial to the environment. In the early phases of art, survival was assured by utility and significance. What we call the art of prehistoric and primitive people was also their science, or means of investigating reality, and their magic, or means of controlling reality. But it cannot be common utility that explains its perseverance, because art that has served no social function other than the aesthetic has survived and propagated, as in recent centuries, with unabated vigor.[4]

Art does not persist by the approval of each successive generation in human history, but by a principle of inertia. Except by the exercise of inconceivable repressive power, we could not stop art, even if we should choose to do so, any more than we could stop language. The comparison does not imply that the survival of art necessarily is assured by its symbolic, communicative function; that is one factor, but others are drives to create and to imitate which may be indifferent to a prospective audience. The impulses that produce art are found in most, if not all humans, and may be related somehow to our survival in evolutionary competition.

Life does not repeatedly appear by spontaneous generation (as was believed not long ago on the evidence of the appearance of bacteria in sealed solutions and maggots in decaying organic matter); nor does art. Every style of the past and present descends in some way from a few geographically and culturally isolated origins in pre-historic times. In the whole span of recorded time, no art can be proven to have been initiated without some stimulus from preceding forms. The most radical shifts of direction invariably have swept away certain features of tradition while adhering to others: the Renaissance threw off some characteristics of late medieval art, but with the aid of still earlier art; and hardly any of the most experimental painters of our time relinquished the Renaissance problems of easel painting. Indeed, our "avant garde" has been unusually and promiscuously historical, in resurrecting Japanese prints, Negro sculpture, Persian miniatures, and so on. Whenever we get the notion that a radical change of direction in the art of the past was wholly without ancestral precedent, it is likely that some evidence is missing. Though all modern forms have roots in a few prehistoric sources, evolution does not follow a straight course; each source produced many offshoots, of which a few survive while the huge majority became extinct.

Natural Selection. According to the principle of natural selection, the evolution of species is the product of differential reproduction occurring genetically, and of the interaction between the organisms produced and their physical and organic environment. Individuals better adapted to successful life in a given environment tend to be favored by their ability to produce more offspring. Natural selection does not favor change over stability; in a relatively stable and congenial environment, mutations are likely to be unfavorable, and certain animals such as the opossum and the bat have managed to survive without much change for over 50,000,000 years; the phenomenon is known as stabilizing selection. But, when the environment alters or becomes more hostile, selection encourages the appearance of characters better adapted to its conditions.

The evolution of the modern horse offers a good example, since it is especially well documented.[5] The line can be traced to a mammal of the Eocene era, perhaps sixty million years ago, called *Eohippus,* a tiny, four-toed browsing creature with a very small brain. His descendant, *Mesohippus,* was nearly twice as large, had three padded toes and was much smarter. This was the end of a simple linear development. From here on, a number of distinct genera emerged of which only one led to the modern horse; in time the remainder disappeared. Most continued as browsers, but in the Miocene era one line (*Parahippus-Merychippus*) made a significant step from browsing to grazing that favored a wholly new kind of tooth composition and structure (thus altering the skull), and digestive system. Meanwhile the rotation of the fore and hind legs had become severely restricted, and the three-toed foot, thus specialized for running, began to operate like a spring, with the aid of ligaments, in order to propel the increased weight at the speed attained by lighter ancestors. One descendant of this group, the *Pliohippus,* lost his auxiliary toes to develop the single hoof of his modern descendant; the most advanced members of this line are already *Equus.*

Opposing Interpretations of the Evolutionary Process. There are two ways to interpret this evidence; the one, which minimizes the factor of chance and the role of the environment, takes many forms, from the extreme of finalism (according to which the modern horse—or man —was "meant to be"; his development was steered along the path it took by an external guiding force, necessarily of a supernatural character) to the more moderate principle of orthogenesis (development-in-a-straight-line;

usually strictly determined by an internal component, though not progressing toward a foreseen goal). The other—natural selection—postulates variations occurring by chance, which gave some horses advantages over others that aided them in escaping predators, in competing for mates, and in producing and protecting offspring. There was no plan involved, and no step in the direction ultimately taken implied any or all of the subsequent steps. At any moment, a number of variants were brought into a world which ultimately was to favor some more than others; the shifting conditions of that world might be as important in horse development as anything peculiarly horsy. Finalism, the first of these interpretations, involves a plan beyond our comprehension and ultimately a Maker of this plan, while natural selection, with its emphasis on the free operation of the genetic mechanism, leaves nothing outside the scope of potential investigation. Both systems have their appeal, but scientists and scholars have no real choice but to accept the latter, as the former ultimately can be handled only by theologians or metaphysicians.

The Function of Natural Selection. The story of the horse, then, is to be explained by the selection of characteristics favoring grazing over browsing to allow a greater range of action—the change occurred at a time when grass was increasing—and the ability to avoid predators by speed of flight rather than by, say, the armor developed by such horse relatives as the rhinoceros. From fossil evidence it is not possible to agree conclusively on the selective advantage of every feature; for example, the general increase in size, which does not occur in a constant development (there were long periods without notable size change and some branches even became smaller). Though the overall evolution can be represented as linear and destined to produce the modern horse, the major trends have been, in fact, anything but predictable. They did not continue previous trends, but represent *shifts* in evolutionary direction (e.g., from short browsing teeth to long grazing teeth; from pad feet to hooves); furthermore, each one occurred over limited spans of time and separately within single lineages. The rate of change was not regular; shifts occurred at an accelerated rate, since transitional forms are disadvantageous (middle-sized teeth would be poorly adapted to either grazing or browsing). Finally, the lines that shifted radically from early branches normally did not *supplant* more primitive ones but shared the earth with them over millions of years, and of course many radical but impractical shifts were snuffed out so quickly as to leave no record.

The Application of Natural Selection to Art. The same problem appears in art history and demands a choice between solutions of the kind once so fiercely debated in biology. Every past style has been interpreted as a linear sequence of achievements progressively nearing the goal of a perfected or "classic" form of that style. Just as the spokesman of orthogenesis would have the line from *Mesohippus* to *Parahippus* aimed in the direction of *Equus,* Notre Dame of Paris and Sens Cathedral may be represented as early and only partially fulfilled attempts to build Amiens, or the Italian "primitives" (revealing word!) as would-be Raphaels. By contrast, the theory of natural selection convincingly explains the apparently systematic evolution of styles toward optimal solutions without relying on a guiding agency.

In the evolution of a style, variants appear in different works of art, of which some are "well adapted" and some not. Adaptation in this sense is the capacity to stimulate emulation among artists and favorable response in the society at large. What makes style evolve is the incorporation of new characters into the complex. Each generation of artists—and of patrons—keeps what it wants from the generation before and rejects what it has no use for. But, as in life, the well adapted variant tends to produce more offspring. Usually the most compelling innovations—and traditions—are kept, but there are also periods when the facile and inconsequential fares better; evolution is not a synonym for progress. There cannot be a predestined or predictable development because the process depends not only on the achievement represented in any work of art but on the ability and desire of later artists and laymen to accept it. The phenomenon of apparent growth toward classic forms (as at Amiens) is explained by the fact that a commanding initial conception poses a problem that challenges generations of artists to refine the solution, and to rephrase the problem itself in terms of intervening solutions. Not all works of art now regarded as masterpieces have been so well received; many produced no

following in their time simply because they were disliked or misunderstood (for example, the late *Pietàs* of Michelangelo).

Radiation. As styles radiate into divergent paths, adapting to different environments, it often happens that the so-called mainstream is less long-lived than a provincial offshoot, since the provinces tend to be conservative and slow to change. The Gothic style of architecture, which spread throughout Europe from the Ile de France in the twelfth and thirteenth centuries was nearly extinct in France by the end of the 1400's, but flourished in a South German branch of delicately vaulted hall churches for another century and a half.

Art historians usually do not speak of a style radiating to produce distinct offshoots, but of one style "succeeding" another. But a true case of succession would be even harder to find in art than in life, where there have been rare and intriguing cases of "phyletic evolution", in which the whole of a single population—always geographically isolated—changes from one species to another without splitting. It is questionable whether there is convincing documentation for a comparable cultural isolation and uniformity; in any case, the typical pattern of historical process is represented by the Renaissance which, though it outlasted the Gothic, did not really succeed it, as demonstrated by the survival of Gothic art so long after Masaccio and Donatello.

The Multiplication of Species and Styles. Early evolutionists explained the origin of new species by sudden gross mutations in individuals (saltations) which then immediately became the source of distinct lines. How these individuals propagated without the simultaneous aid of more-or-less normal mates and a compatible environment could not be explained, and recent theories of speciation have made the population rather than the unit the prime object of study. Similarly, the initiation of major new styles cannot be attributed to the isolated creation of a single great artist. They can be recognized and defined only in terms of related characters in large groups of works, and the great artist is the one that epitomizes a tendency and stimulates certain trends in its evolution.

Speciation normally proceeds gradually and imperceptibly, though radical and relatively sudden shifts in direction may occur, as with some of the horse's ancestors. The same is true of art, though the shifts often are called, misleadingly, "revolutions",[6] a concept that prompts historians to refer loosely to a "first Renaissance building" (Foundling Hospital, Florence) or a "first Cubist picture" (Picasso's *Demoiselles d'Avignon*), as if those works were miraculously successful mutants that sprang into the artist's mind without preparation.

Dialectic theories of art, particularly in Germany, have encouraged revolutionary rather than evolutionary interpretations of history. So the change from late Archaic to early Classic Greek sculpture has been represented as a revolution overthrowing a refined, linear and abstract style in favor of a more vigorous, blocky and representational one. The metaphor of modern evolution offers an interpretation of the same phenomena without, however, demanding breaks or leaps in the continuity of culture.

The Interplay of Innovation and Environment in Evolution. The emergence of period styles, like that of species, is studied in terms of aggregates; but art history, unlike biology, cannot ignore the role of the individual. Differential variations occurring genetically can be attributed to chance, but variations in works of art are consciously willed (or produced unconsciously and consciously capitalized on). So the prime mechanism in the evolution of art is the individual imagination.

This is not to say that the artist alone controls evolution. Change is not essentially generated by what artists want, but by the effect of the works they produce—artists' manifestos and theoretical writings reveal what a difference there can be. Those who aim to direct evolution can only orient their work within or away from tradition and hope that contemporaries and successors may follow the lead. Once a work leaves the studio, the process of natural selection begins to operate: the cultural environment, by accepting or rejecting it, provides the structure of the evolution. In a limited sense, this selective process is also creative; though it does not produce the raw materials—the variants—it determines the extent to which they prosper or decline and the way in which they are integrated into the culture. So the course of a style is determined by the nature of the *interplay* between works of art and their environment.

Adaptation: the Environment of Art. Since life depends on a dynamic equilibrium between an organism and its environment, the principle of adaptation (adjustment to the environment) is the core of the theory of natural selection. An organism that has changed through differential variation prospers only if its new characteristics are adapted to its environment and, conversely, a change in the environment favors only organisms that can adapt to the new conditions. This environment includes the physical area(s) in which the organism lives, and the organic population of the area(s), including members of its own species.

The adaptation of works of art must be measured within a cultural and a physical environment. The cultural environment is constituted in general by the society in which a work of art is produced, and in particular by those who use art consciously.

The obstacle to applying the principle of adaptation to works of art in their cultural environment has been the realization that in recent times the most meaningful art apparently has been rejected and ridiculed by the environment, and thus seems to be poorly adapted. But this has been due to our curious failure to admit that artists—in the capacity of a public—constitute an important factor in the environment. Artists, indeed, provide the essential mechanism of evolution; if they reject an innovation, it cannot be sustained, no matter how many others approve it; if they accept one, it cannot perish, though it have no other sponsors. If we do not think of artists as components of the environment and consumers of art, it is because we cast them in a romantic role—rejected and isolated by society, economic failures. Yet for a century and a half the evolution of style has been dominated by "rejected" artists, while their colleagues who adapted to prevailing tastes failed to keep their styles alive. Cézanne illustrates the point; few people understood his work, but through those few it changed the world. Art needs a public, but not a socially dominant one; a handful of sympathetic artists can constitute the most influential class of all. The effectiveness of artist as public is proven by the fact that most of the finest criticism since Vasari has been done by artists or writers closely associated with artists.

The evolution of style, then, is not necessarily guided by taste, though in every age some or all artists are led or pushed by patrons and social pressures—especially in eras when all art is commissioned and performs specific functions. Art adapted to the prevailing taste[7] may prove to be overspecialized for long-term survival, since taste is one of the most changeable aspects of culture. In nearly every historical instance of conflict between what artists produce independently and what fashion demands, the judgment of time has shown the former to be better fit.

"Survival of the Fittest." Darwin's term, "survival of the fittest" (or "struggle for survival"), which appealed so much to *laissez-faire* capitalists, schoolmasters and diplomats of the last century, is misleading. To be "fit" or adapted in an evolutionary sense is not, as is commonly thought, to be exceptionally powerful and far-ranging; if that were so, jungles would contain only lions, which would then die of starvation. The defenseless mouse and slug are as "fit" as the king of beasts, and fitter than his relative the sabre-tooth tiger, which failed to survive. Within species the same applies; human evolution shows that intellectual ingenuity can compensate amply for lack of physical power (as illustrated by the comic-book image of the superior being from outer space as a man with a tiny, feeble body, an enormous head, and antennae symbolizing extraordinary cerebral equipment); and that aborigines with a stone-age technology can survive as well as highly civilized atom-smashers. So fitness is not a determinate condition; a population may be more-or-less fit, and in the process of improving its fitness, or it may survive for long periods only to be replaced by another still more fit.

Similarly, individuals within any population vary in fitness; extreme cases are monsters incapable of adaptation to any environment (in art, incompetent or meaningless work); more relevant are variants that might function successfully in a somewhat different environment (animals with coloration poorly suited to their habitat; art that is not welcomed in its time or place). Since these variants may be as vigorous and as fertile as their fitter relatives, their unfitness cannot be taken as evidence of their intrinsic inferiority.[8] The implications for history and criticism are clear: a position that, in the evolutionary metaphor, a work of art may be evaluated according to its fitness—in the sense of adjust-

ment to the taste of its time and place—cannot be sustained; there are many degrees of fitness, and even *unfitness* has no necessary value implications. To say that the rejection of a work of art by its cultural environment is good or bad is to judge the environment as well as the work.

Stability and Change. Adaptation is not synonymous with change; the conservative Egyptian culture nurtured a style that evolved less in the course of millennia than recent styles did in a generation; it quickly extinguished the only radical shift in its history—the style of the eighteenth dynasty—in favor of a return to something like the previous *status quo.* But the term "stability" as applied to a culture or style is relative; absolute stability is stagnation. When artists reproduce patterns without individual variation, their art soon is extinguished for lack of vitality; this is comparable to inbreeding in organisms, which tends to inhibit adaptation. In art or in life, a line is strengthened by individual variation and moderate admission of foreign strains, although excessive outbreeding may weaken adaptation to specific local conditions. Variation, then, cannot be thought of as the antithesis of stability; it is rather a prerequisite for it. Styles can be sustained over long time spans only by admitting constant inventiveness to challenge the imagination of their practitioners.

In unstable and complex cultures such as those of recent centuries, the arts change often. It appears that the rate of change in Western art has been accelerating regularly; but we lack perspective on our own time, and someday the evolution of Florentine art of the fifteenth century may seem to be faster than that of modern architecture, for example, which leveled off to a relatively stable condition after a period of rapid change from 1910 to 1935.

Do Styles "Decline"? The extinction of styles in the past is often described as the end product of a gradual "decline" from a classic moment of maximum vigor. The source of this image is an archaic adaptation of biology to criticism represented in Vasari's statement (1568) that style, "like human bodies, has a birth, a growth, an ageing and a death". Vasari's metaphor may have satisfied Renaissance humanists and their descendants, but it obscures more than it illuminates. The individual works which we group into styles are not organically inter-dependent as cells are in the body, nor is the so-called "life cycle" alike in different styles—it varies in character as much as in duration. The cyclical analogy warps criticism by implying that the early phases of every style are infantile or primitive while the later phases are enfeebled by age.

The evolutionary metaphor does not constrict criticism because the life and extinction of species obeys no fixed pattern. When extinction is due to a change in environment, the species itself may not decline in vigor but only in numbers; in other words, it may remain perfectly adapted to an environment that is in the process of shrinking away. With this analogy we can explain styles that disappear without in any way degenerating—the Gothic, for example, which was vital and creative at the time it was being displaced by the Renaissance: brilliant innovations of the late medieval International style and English Perpendicular architecture were contemporaneous to those of Masaccio and Brunelleschi; Monet's *Water Lilies* series, now so highly praised and priced, were painted long after Impressionism had been "supplanted" by other styles (one of them absurdly called "Post-Impressionism"—imagine calling horses "Post-Parahippi"!). The new cultural environment to which styles adapt gradually replaces the old, but the old lingers on in a segment of the same population or away from the great centers, and fosters the traditional forms. So "old" styles do not suddenly vanish, as they are apt to do in handbooks and lecture courses, as new ones emerge; but continue on until the environment to which they are adapted is quite overwhelmed by a younger, expanding culture. Occasionally, however, an environment is bypassed and isolated in the expansion of a new culture, either because it is provincial or because its government or religion opposes change; then its art may indeed decline through hardening of the arteries, as did Byzantine art, which the Eastern Orthodox church has kept half-alive for centuries after it ceased to be creative.

The Impact of Art on the Environment. The adaptation of art to the environment is not a one-way path: the environment also adjusts to art. As the introduction of new bacteria or germicides into a balanced ecology can cause far-reaching changes, so the introduction of a new art form (or the disappearance of an old one) may alter everyone's conceptual processes. Once we learn to interpret a radically new kind of visual communication, we look at everything in a somewhat different way. Modern Expressionism, for example, aided a re-evaluation of the past that brought Tintoretto and El Greco to the fore, somewhat to the disadvantage of Correggio and Murillo. But the impact of art is felt beyond its own sphere: in the fifteenth century, the interest of artists, and of Leonardo da Vinci in particular, in problems of illusion and of proportion promoted the progress of experimental science: Vesalius without the background of early Renaissance art would never have been known outside of Padua.

Today, the potential effect of art on the cultural environment is enormously increased by photographs and the mass media. Books and magazines produced in a few urban centers are homogenizing the visual diet of the entire world, with the result that paintings and buildings in Japan are sometimes indistinguishable from those in Denmark and Brazil. The adaptation in this case is not primarily to a local culture, but to the world market, but it is certain that local cultures will be increasingly affected by this trend.

Adaptations to the Physical Environment. Climate and topography have not changed much since the era of cave art, but they do vary in different parts of the world, and are responsible for differences among local styles. They affect architecture more than the figurative arts because its function is to modify the natural environment for aesthetic and practical purposes. Adjustments include those necessary for structural stability (defenses against wind and snow loads, moisture, fire, etc.) and for the comfort of inhabitants (control of light, heat and cold, air, noise, pollution, etc.), and they affect the design of roofs, windows, open and closed areas, and the choice of materials and colors. Modern building technology, however, has produced sufficient environmental defenses to make the same design viable in the most diverse climates, thus promoting the trend to global uniformity.

The more portable a work of art is, the less local conditions affect it. Variation in easel painting or graphic art is not usually attributable to the purely physical environment; also, most portable art in our culture is kept in buildings, isolated from natural conditions.

Specialization. Following the direction of our culture, architecture has become increasingly specialized in function. At one time, a community required only dwellings, a religious center, a marketplace and perhaps recreational facilities, and a house was only a sheltered room with a hearth. Today a huge variety of structures is required, from hamburger stands to cyclotrons. The rate of specialization has not been uniform; at the height of the Roman Empire, architecture was more varied than in the Middle Ages and Renaissance, when forensic basilicas, baths, amphitheatres, nymphaea, circuses, gymnasia and other Roman types of buildings were not required, and a few types of domestic and ecclesiastical structures sufficed. By contrast, the figural arts have become less specialized since the late Renaissance, when they began to be produced for the market. Apart from rare ecclesiastical and civic commissions, modern painting and sculpture are done for no place and nobody in particular and function either in the parlors and offices of the well-to-do or in museums, where art is held in suspension by the elimination of environment; in museums, every culture is on the same footing.

Conclusion. An evolutionary history of art explains changes in style through individual variations without implying a directing agent or a predetermined goal. It solves the dilemma of a discipline divided between those whose principles of historical change devaluate the uniqueness of the individual achievement, and those who appreciate the uniqueness but slight histor-ical processes. The former attribute change in style to agencies outside the control of artists: *determinism,* expressed in terms either of cycles of growth-and-decline or of action-and-reaction, suggests inevitable patterns of development; *social history* ultimately makes the artist merely a chronicler of his times; the latter, *connoisseurs* and *critics,* discuss single works or single artists, but usually not the broader problems of style evolution.

On the evolutionary model the variations or innovations tend to be almost imperceptible in stable cultures and to be more abrupt and radical in fluid cultures. Some innovations are incorporated into traditional styles, and others become the root of new styles which often grow alongside the older ones. Poorly adapted innovations either are summarily rejected or, if they are potentially viable, lie dormant to act upon a later, more congenial environment. So, while the individual imagination generates change, society, including artists, guides its rate and direction; but only by post-facto selectivity; the environment can prompt imaginative solutions by posing challenging problems, but cannot itself formulate the solutions.

To emphasize imaginative innovation is not to make a virtue of change, except in the limited sense that a total absence of variation ossifies an art. The measure that evolutionary theory offers to criticism is rather that of adaptation. The finest works of art are those whose message is sufficiently profound and universal to warrant and win respect not only at the place and time in which they were made, but everywhere and at all times.

1. This essay owes much to Professor George Gaylord Simpson's extensive and imaginative criticism of an earlier draft, for which I am most grateful.

2. For example, the contribution of genetics, a science manifestly inapplicable to cultural history, finally justified Darwin and revealed the mechanics of natural selection; but genetics has refined, without altering, the basic principles of evolution that are useful to historians.

3. Professor Simpson reminded me that termination without issue is not the only form of extinction in the biological world. In life as in art, a line may be extinguished by being transformed into something new.

4. The change from cave culture to the present resembles an evolutionary process in which art is liberated progressively from a subordinate role: the magical significance of its early phase is followed by the religious, and ultimately, in recent times, by the autonomous. But such an image revives the fallacy of evolution as progress; it is not concerned with art itself, but with its *function* in society.

5. See George Gaylord Simpson, *Horses,* New York (1951).

6. There are no revolutions in art. A work of art does not contain propositions and therefore cannot take a negative position. If it differs from earlier works, it may suggest an alternative path, but it does not diminish the powers of its predecessors.

7. The term "prevailing taste" is an oversimplification; there are often several tastes in a culture, each representing what biologists call an "ecological niche" that is likely to be filled by a different style the moment it is vacated by an abandoned one. A recent illustration is the niche created by American banking and industry, which in the last generation required eclectic architecture and since the Second World War demands modern "International Style" buildings, generally without insisting on quality.

8. An intriguing example is the phenomenon of "industrial melanism" studied in peppered moths of the manufacturing areas of Great Britain. The progressive blackening of the landscape by smoke and soot has selectively favored dark colored moths, as predators found light ones easier to spot. The light moths are no less vigorous than they were in the days of their ascendancy, and perhaps, if the age of atomic power helps to brighten the industrial environment, they may again become the more fit. The role of environmental blight as the cause of unfitness and the promoter of variants suggests revealing parallels in cultural history.

SELECTED BIBLIOGRAPHY

Since this paper was sent to press, the subject has been treated exhaustively and with great learning by Thomas Munro in *Evolution in the Arts and Other Theories of Culture History,* Cleveland/New York (1963).

Ackerman, James S., and Carpenter, Rhys, *Art and Archaeology,* Englewood Cliffs (1963).

Bertalanffy, Ludwig von, *Problems of Life,* New York (1960).

Blum, Harold F., *Time's Arrow and Evolution,* 2nd ed., New York (1962).

Comfort, Alex, *Darwin and the Naked Lady; Discursive Essays on Biology and Art,* New York (1962).

Hoagland, Hudson, and Burhoe, Ralph, eds., *Evolution and Man's Progress,* New York and London (1962); originally published as the Summer, 1962 issue of *Daedalus.*

Huxley, T. H., *Evolution, the Modern Synthesis,* London (1942).

Jepsen, G. L., *et al.,* eds., *Genetics, Paleontology and Evolution,* Princeton (1949).

Kroeber, Alfred L., *Configurations of Culture Growth,* Berkeley and Los Angeles (1944).

Kubler, George, *The Shape of Time,* New Haven (1962).

Mayr, Ernst, *Animal Species and Evolution,* Cambridge, Mass. (1963).

Oparin, A. I., *The Origin of Life,* 2nd ed., N.Y. (1953).

Schapiro, Meyer, "Style," *Anthropology Today,* ed. A. L. Kroeber, Chicago (1953), p. 287; reprinted in *Aesthetics Today,* ed. M. Philipson, New York (1961), p. 81.

Simpson, George G., *Horses; the Story of the Horse Family . . .* New York (1951).

———, *Life, an Introduction to Biology,* with C. S. Pittendrigh and L. H. Tiffany, New York (1957).

———, *The Meaning of Evolution,* New Haven (1949; 1960).

———, *Principles of Animal Taxonomy,* New York (1961).

Smith, John M., *The Theory of Evolution,* Harmondsworth and Baltimore (1958).

Tax, Sol, ed., *Evolution after Darwin,* I: *The Evolution of Life,* Chicago (1960).

Teilhard de Chardin, Pierre, *The Phenomenon of Man,* New York (1961).

GILLO DORFLES

THE ROLE OF MOTION IN OUR VISUAL HABITS AND ARTISTIC CREATION

There is considerable evidence that man is usually not immediately aware of certain profound transformations which occur in his normal life of relationships, so that only later do these transformations become obvious to him. Because of his conditioning by the habits, customs, traditions, the "routines" of his *modus vivendi,* he is scarcely conscious of the development of certain events which set up important transformations in his sensory, perceptive and proprioceptive activities, causing a reaction throughout entire areas of his productive and communicative activity.

A phenomenon of this kind does not cease to surprise psychologists, anthropologists, aestheticians. Many still believe that man's "state of consciousness"—of receptivity, of creativity—is stable and immutable. However, the introduction of a new mechanical discovery, a new food, a new medicine, a new system of playing a game, of sport, of art, and so on, is enough to profoundly change his consciousness and his activities.

A typical example is the discovery of photography. Here is a "technical means"—before it is an artistic or communicative form—which, in a short span of time, has not only changed our perceptive and visualizing capacities, but has caused unimaginable transformations in the field of art—the very revolt and self-assertion of non-objective art can perhaps be connected with the spread of that technical-expressive medium. Photography has brought about an incredible extension of our visual panorama and has given birth to that "New Landscape" which Gyorgy Kepes has treated so amply and acutely.

Another element responsible for profound metamorphoses in our whole manner of visualizing the external world—and also our internal world—is *motion.* In evaluating the cultural, philosophical, psychological, and aesthetic phenomena of a specific epoch, one cannot leave out daily experiences. For this reason the class of phenomena which we can group under the term motion must be considered one of the most significant dimensions to which present-day existence is subject, from both perceptive and specifically aesthetic points of view.

Motion, we know, relates to dynamics. Dynamics is the action of a force on an object, an organism, an event. Through this dynamism developed in time, motion implies another fundamental concept, that of *tempo.*

(Let us not forget—to go back to works of older philosophers—that for Aristotle [*Physics,* 219 a], time "is the number of motion, according to what is before and what is beyond", and that for Hobbes time is "the representation of motion in that one imagines in it a first thing and an after thing, or a succession".) Such considerations might seem—and are, in fact—obvious. One could also note that the concepts of time and of dynamism, as well as that of kinetics, have always existed, and that, from Heracleitus on, man has been considered to be immersed in an incessant stream of moments relentlessly following each other, conditioning his existence and his *Weltanschauung.*

What is it, then, which distinguishes present-day motion from that of the past? I believe that it is a question of its artificiality, of the intervention of mechanical and technological forces to produce a tempo different from the natural, physiological and cosmological tempo. The motion of an airplane, of an automobile, of a jet, of a missile—that is, of motorized machines—has nothing whatever to do with man's physiological motion, where the impetus of his movement is implicit in his physical constitution and not extrinsic to it. I believe that many of the artistic manifestations of our day—and not only artistic ones—relate to this new aspect of "life in motion". Some of the innovations of recent architecture which tends to detach itself from the mass and weight of the trilithic system, some of the pictorial and plastic manifestations, the very multiplication of sports like skiing, bobsledding and hockey (leaving out those which directly utilize mechanical means): all depend on the impulse determined by the "life in motion" in which the man of our time finds himself.

It should not surprise us that, among the most efficacious examples of modern advertising (I have elsewhere[1]) pointed out the importance of advertising, from both sociological and aesthetic points of view, as a most potent means of information, capable of spreading a specific graphic and pictorial "taste" to large strata of the population), are those which are based on the movement of images—animated cartoons, or short cinema or television films. Figures in motion produce with astonishing efficacy that compelling effect, that "sense of causality" (so well described by Michotte[2]) of which, consciously or not, advertising men avail themselves. And, besides the "causal" efficacy, one must take

1. Boeing XB–47 Stratojet in rocket-assisted take-off.

2. Patterns of moving car lights. Student photograph, M.I.T

into account the "spellbinding" effect of the image in motion and the possibility of arousing through it, simply by means of the perceptive mechanism those "subliminal suggestions" of which advertising sometimes makes use and which would be entirely unthinkable in sequences of static photographs.

As long as the movements of man, of other living organisms, of things, could be related to the essential rhythms of nature—years, months, days, the beating of the pulse, breathing, menstrual periods, and so on—the passage of time was obviously understood as deeply rooted in the very nature of creatures. The speed attained by man, even when he had recourse to forces not his own, for example, a horse driven at a gallop, was still always identifiable with natural phenomena.

Today—or from the beginning of the technological era—*speed* is basic to our life or relationships. Pressured by continuous dynamic impulses, surrounded by an incessant tide of motion, we have become dominated by this new dimension; often we can succeed in conceiving of life and its "products" only as evolving in a continuous and persistent *becoming*.

In the field of perception and artistic creation, which especially interests us here, we shall turn our attention first to the new forms of art determined by motion and definitely bound to it, rather than to those which have only been superficially influenced by it.

Other writers may examine the rise of artistic forms superficially influenced by motion, such as Cubism, Futurism, "plastic dynamism", and painting which tries to introduce the "dimension of time" into the static canvas. Still others may consider as interesting experiments with art more properly defined as "dynamic", like the motorized sculptures of Tinguely, the mobiles of Calder or Chadwick, of Munari or Kenneth Martin; or the works of artists such as Vasarely, Soto, Rot and Bury; which seek an element of motion or at least vibration by exploiting tricks of texture that make the image unstable, thereby dynamizing it.

However, I shall not dwell further on such examples. I have mentioned them only to demonstrate the existence, in the field of visual art—once considered absolutely static, the art referred to by Lessing as the "art of space"—of a new element which is decidedly dynamic and chronological. Instead, I wish to analyze a little more thoroughly the modifications which determine

1

2

3

4

3. Fernand Legér. *The City,* 1919. Solomon R. Guggenheim Museum.

4. Umberto Boccioni. *Synthesis of Human Dynamism,* 1912.

our attitude toward the external world and the artistic world as a result of the presence around us of the remarkable contribution of motion.

I should also say, before I go on, that one must always take into account the haziness of the idea man has of himself and of his different "states of consciousness": each individual is conscious of his existence and of his own perceptive activity only insofar as it is part of a human collectivity; yet he cannot represent himself as having gathered all the phenomenal data which this collectivity offers to him; meanwhile, he separates himself from the collectivity in the same moment that he sets himself up to judge it. Our statements about the environmental situation in which we find ourselves will always be guilty of this limitation.

At this point I should like to fix, at least provisionally, the limits and areas of the modifications induced by motion in our lives, and establish some essential points:

1. The effect and efficacy of motion—or better, of speed, motion which is rapid in respect to the "norm" established as basic to our physiological, ancestral rhythm—must be considered in terms of *active* and *passive*, according to whether motion is passively undergone or actively lived. Such a distinction seems to me fundamental, since one's attitude in regard to motion can vary notably in the second case. More often than it would seem, we have a passive attitude toward the dynamics of events which surround us. As a result, such dynamics exercise on us, not a dynamizing effect which would intensify our perceptive and cogitative activity, but an effect which is compelling, actually spellbinding, blunting and clouding our normal perceptive and conscious "waking" faculties.

2. The sudden transformations resulting from the speed of the normal panorama in which we are placed have conditioned our habitual life of relationships. As a direct consequence we must consider: a) the *new possibilities of visualization and of representation induced by the transformations of the natural panorama seen in speed,* the view from the moving train, from the airplane, from the helicopter, etc; and b) the *effects which motion exercises on the design of objects, substantially modifying the forms,* the creation of aerodynamic forms of objects produced by industry, and also what happens to the forms of static objects with dynamic characteristics which have resulted from motor situations previously unknown, etc.

3. We must take into account finally the communicative and aesthetic forms which have sprung up as a result of dynamic mechanisms and are based on them, such as cinematography and television, and their influence in turn on the human personality and on other arts.

Referring to point one of the above outline, I wish to point out that, on the whole, the emotional and moving element in our aesthetic and, in general, perceptive evaluations is closely bound to the effect of motion. Michotte also observes this: "When we are present at certain motor performances—the dance, acrobatics, tennis, football . . . our movements correspond with those which we are seeing and seem led by them; our hand or foot beats out automatically . . . the rhythm of the observed movements."[3] There is therefore a parallelism between movements which are seen and those which are produced. In other cases the spectator actually repeats the miming and the action he watches on the stage.[4] In such cases one reaches a "real merging of the visual data and the proprioceptive tactile-kinaesthetic data. . . ." Naturally such phenomena are already well-known and can be made to fall within a larger area, such as that of empathy.[5]

Motion—and this is the point which interests us—is capable of favoring and intensifying the empathetic element (which surely exists also in many static phenomena) because, through the transmission of a peculiar rhythm, it "sets in motion" the innermost rhythmic structures of the human constitution.

But, while man has been conditioned ever since his appearance in the world, and is constituted in all his physiological structure to obey and respond to a "cosmic rhythm" (bound obviously to breathing, to cardiac pulsation, to the mysterious rhythms of the universe, alternating like day and night, the tides, the months, etc.), it is probable that only in our era has he found himself in contact with mechanical rhythms which interfere profoundly with his interior rhythms. From this originates the trauma caused to the cellular or micro-colloidal connections of his brain, and also the probable induction of states of consciousness and of emotional pressures which are unfathomed and even dangerous.

What would happen, indeed, if we let ourselves be carried away by this "rhythmic sympathy" in every case?

Only think of what happens when we travel on fast trains where the rhythm of the train is much faster than that of our pulse and breathing. Often we try to "match" the rhythm of the train with our rhythm, only to realize at once the impossibility of making our organic rhythm coincide and harmonize with the mechanical one. This is a phenomenon which occurs every time we are confronted with analogous motor situations. Even if we are not able to adjust our body rhythms to the mechanical ones, it is possible that these motor pressures can create a disequilibrium more or less equal to that which I would like to call our "dynamic body scheme".

As on the train, when we see the objects and landscape in the foreground passing with great speed, and so concentrate our attention on the background which appears almost immobile, so it happens in other cases as well that our attention fixes on a few static elements, passing over the dynamized ones, or at least the excessively dynamized ones. We can therefore assert, as a general law, that our attention usually centers on elements whose dynamism does not exceed a certain quotient of rapidity, so that we have an *increase of efficacy* due to the dynamics of an object, in comparison with the same object in static condition, and a *diminution of efficacy* when this dynamism exceeds a certain limit, to the point of annulling all efficacy through an excessive rapidity of motion.

If we go back now to the second point indicated above, that is to the examination of some transformation undergone by perceived objects as a consequence of motion and the various visualizing possibilities due to it, we can make some supplementary observations. A comparison with the normal reading of a written passage will be helpful. When we read a book, the printed letters usually are not perceived as such, distinctly and separately (the most elementary notions of *Gestalt* teach us this), but as a whole, organized with a clear "signaling" function which permits us to "jump" from the initial perceptive moment to the image-making response elicited by the letters. By the same token, we can assert that many of our kinetic perceptions often cancel themselves at the very moment in which they are set up, creating of every object, of every event, a signaling element capable of transmitting sufficiently precise information. I have taken the example of reading (and could have

taken that of deciphering a page of music) because in itself reading implies a kinetic activity, a journey through time, that acquires its peculiar character only through virtue of such a journey. Now, the step is short from the case of the journey made by the eye running over the lines printed in a book, devouring with incredible rapidity the letters which compose the text without really hesitating over any of them, to the eye's journey traveling over a landscape through a train window. We "read" the landscape through the window of a train, of an airplane, of an automobile, just as we read the lines of the poem, the notes of the symphony. Moreover, this reading is made possible by a "symbolization of kinetic elements" already previously established, without which the right interpretation of the given phenomena would be impossible, or at least problematical; nor would it be "legible" without a previously established semanticizing. The reading of the elements which are kinetically perceived is made possible by the fact that a particular symbolic semantic heritage is established in advance, whose "terms" we are progressively made aware of and participate in.

Now we come briefly to the third point of our premise, to the new communicative and aesthetic forms which have arisen as a consequence of the dynamic mechanisms, especially those which have been defined in the "new art" constituted by cinema and television presentations.

One should not be surprised that it is in our era that the advent of cinematography was made possible—and I might say, almost indispensable. For the first time in history, man can be present at a performance made possible by the fact that immobile images can be put in motion. It is, in fact, motion which offers to this art its incredible communicative and creative possibilities. But more curious and interesting is the fact that seeing figures projected on the screen move as if they were real happens—so the technicians tell us—thanks to the "stereokinetic effect"[6] through which a two-dimensional image acquires, as a result of motion, a plasticity and solidity it would not otherwise have. Even on the two-dimensional screen, the spectator succeeds in "living" a three-dimensional and plastic reality.

One of the things that differentiates the cinema from still photography and from the theater is its apparently absolute identifiability with the phenomenal world.

The "setting in motion" of images allows them a verisimilitude they would not otherwise have. (This is a given fact which one can easily verify by observing the tricks often used by advertising films or newsreels: a static image is presented on the screen, which, at a given point, is set in motion; or vice versa, the film sequence is suddenly arrested, leaving petrified and macabrely immobile figures which until then had appeared in motion and therefore "alive". The effect thus obtained is that of a dimensional flattening: the disappearance of the stereokinetic effect immediately takes away the plasticity and the apparent spatial depth of the scene. The loss of this phenomenal quality makes the image immediately sink again into its limbo of disembodied phantasmagory.) The research of numerous authors has been centered on this phenomenon, but I do not intend to dwell here on its importance from a perceptive point of view. What is now important to me is to define how cinematography forces us to find ourselves constantly confronted by "artistic fantasies" which have the appearance of reality. Film fantasies are, within certain limits, comparable to the dream fantasies of our nocturnal life and, as such, carry over into our waking consciousness "nocturnal" and hallucinated images, like those of our dreams.[7]

Attendance at a cinema or television performance elicits various extremely bizarre phenomena which must be considered adjuncts of our epoch. The spectator is accustomed to register kinetic sequences, developed in time, but in a time—or better, in a duration—which is not that of normal life, but which can be slowed up or accelerated, and is above all imaginary. The information which the spectator receives through the film accustoms him to jumps in time, to retrogradations, to chronological and spatial coercions, so that at the end of the performance he finds himself in possession of an accumulation of data entirely different from that which the experience of normal life furnishes him. And what is more serious, these data are not considered, as is usually true in the other arts, as "imaginings", as "fantasies", but often, because of their apparent realism, as if they were the mirror of an effective reality.

There are many examples of this "naturalistic surrender" to motion which is capable of increasing our perceptive faculties through technical tricks. I could cite, among others, the effect of "travelling" (i.e., when

6

7

8

an object in motion is accompanied by the motion of the camera), or the use of the "panoramica" which follows the foreground to permit the extension of a movement which would otherwise go out of the immediate field of the screen. These and similar cases teach us that cinematography is based substantially on the "manipulation of motion", not only because it has made motion the medium of its artistic language, but also because it has given motion a particular intensification and a particular capacity for metamorphosis; we can say that the cinema has taught us much about the possibilities of our motor perception. There is no doubt that such an upsetting of our common visual and kinetic perceptions is destined to cause some disequilibrium and some modification in our mode of conceiving "reality". The future will tell us at what point there may be a real peril for us—both ethical and aesthetic—in these manifestations.

From what I have stated above, one could infer that I believe that our human nature is formed by quietness and staticness rather than by motion; that is, that the state of quietness is better suited to a sane and normal situation. This is not entirely correct: undoubtedly motion must be considered as an indispensable alternative to quiet. However, episodes involving motion, to be properly understood and "live", must be transitory and must present some kind of *discontinuity*. The dance, for example, understood in its highest significance of sacred dance, of artistic performance close to ritual, or music and all the other examples of "arts of time" (theater, ballet, pantomime), are certainly based on a succession of movement and pause, *discontinuous movements,* whose duration is never subjected to the inflexible continuity of mechanical tempo. Only in our day has it happened that one finds oneself immersed in a persistent, uninterrupted motor situation, which is protracted for a considerable length of time, as in the case of the cinema or of television, and, outside the artistic field, when we find ourselves transported for hours by mechanical conveyances.

To summarize, on the broadest lines, some of the notions we have expounded in these notes (which, obviously, can only be a basis on which to build a subsequent stricter elaboration of data), we can state that our epoch—roughly speaking, from the beginning of this century or from the end of the preceding one—has witnessed the appearance of a series of phenomena, all previously unknown, which will probably change substantially our physio-psychological personality and so our rapport with the external world.

Our perceiving faculties change as a consequence of the intervention of mechanical motion. If we wish to pin down these mutations in several essential points, we can state the following:

1. A greater efficacy of time and a greater awareness of time;
2. A different perceptive basis in respect to the external world;
3. The tendency to create dynamic works of art;
4. The need to express and describe "states of mind" due to kinetic perception;
5. The dissociation of man from chronological, physiological, and cosmic time, and his adherence (which is more or less dangerous) to technical, mechanical time.

I am far from having exhausted the theme which I proposed to investigate; I hope that other authors will add to it, especially in the field of the arts and psychology. But to close my discussion I should like to add some notes on an aspect of motion which does not exist as such in our environment, but which, from a theoretical and experimental point of view, offers some interest: I mean the problem of "kinetic inversion", of *reverse motion.* The question of irreversibility has been widely studied and discussed by physicists, mathematicians and philosophers,[8] but in aesthetics there exist some careful observations regarding the possibility of *reversible journeys through time:* students of old Flemish counterpoint know this as well as students of the more recent twelve-tone system.

The question of reverse motion extends also to the film (there are examples of sequences used in reverse to achieve a surrealistic effect, which have been exploited in several films[9]), to the dance and to tape-recorder music which, as shown in interesting studies,[10] acquires new characteristics as a consequence of such inversion. Indeed in the case of music it has been shown that in such instances music loses "semantic" elements while it preserves aesthetic elements. I cannot elaborate here on these interesting experiments, for which I refer the reader to the work of Moles.[11] Instead, what I should like to clarify is how motor reversibility allows us to

9. Aerial view of a forest in the snow. (*Photo Courtesy Lockwood, Kessler and Bartlett*)

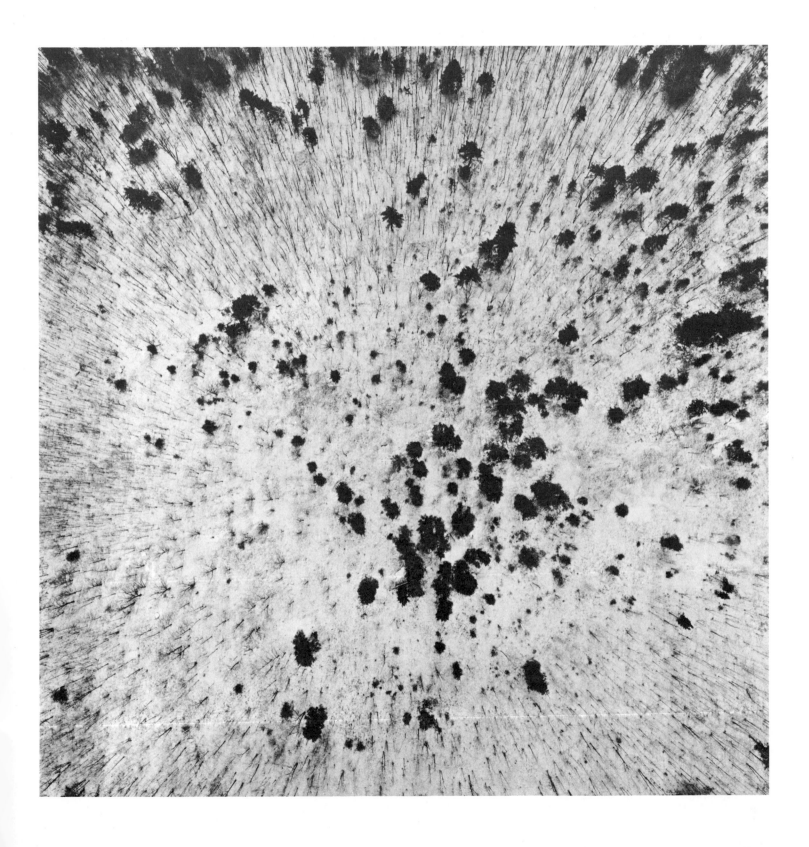

conceive of the existence of a reverse journey through time, something absolutely unknown to periods preceding ours. This reverse journey indicates the possibility of transversing time in two directions, in the same way that one travels through space. Numerous examples (science fiction makes ample use of them) tell us of "time machines", of returning to the origins of the world, of trips backwards at supersonic speed, etc.

All this demonstrates that in our time we are developing a much clearer concept of the *contingent character of chronological reality,* and of the problematical quality of the temporal dimension. The incredible ac-

celeration of our motor possibilities, the incessantly increasing kinetic panorama which surrounds us, the occurrence of physical experiments which denote the possibility of conquering the "barrier" of physiological and chronological time, have caused the chronological entity to lose its absoluteness and its identity, and to break up. We are disposed to accept the appearance of extra-temporal, contra-temporal phenomena, and to admit an inversion and an obliteration of time and of movement. In a future era of the creative, imaginative and perceptive activity of man, these phenomena may well become fundamental principles.

1. See my book, *Divenire delle Arti,* Einaudi, Torino (1959).

2. Albert Michotte, *La perception de la causalité,* Louvain (1946).

3. A. Michotte van den Berck, "La participation émotionelle du spectateur à l'écran," in *Revue internationale de Filmologie* (X:35:1960), p. 65.

4. *Ibid.*

5. See the critique by Rudolf Arnheim, *Arte e Percezione visiva,* Feltrinelli, Milano (1962), pp. 354, 360.

6. *Cf.* Cesare Musatti, "Sui fenomeni stereocinetici," in *Archivio Italiano di Psicologia* (1924:2), "Sulla plasticità reale stereocinetica cinematografica," in *Archivio Italiano di Psicologia* (1929:1), "Les phenomènes stéréocinétiques et les effets stéréoscopiques du cinema," in *Revue de Filmologie* (1957).

7. On the oneiric qualities of the film *cf.* the paper delivered by Cesare Musatti at the *Prima Conferenza Internazionale d'Informazione Visiva,* Milano (July, 1961). *Cf.* also the papers delivered at the same congress by R. Barthes and G. Cohen-Séat.

8. See the study by Enzo Paci, "Il Significato dell' irreversibile," in *Aut Aut* (I:1951), p. 11, with references to the theories of Cassirer, Whitehead, and Heisenberg, and to the concept of entropy.

9. *Cf.* the interesting study by Maya Deren, "Cinematography: The Creative Use of Reality," in *Daedalus* (Winter: 1960), p. 158: "Another unique image which the camera can yield is reverse motion. When used meaningfully, it does not convey so much a sense of backward movement spatially, but rather an undoing of time. One of the most memorable uses of this occurs in Cocteau's *Blood of a Poet....*"

10. A. A. Moles, *Théorie de l'information et perception esthétique,* Flammarion, Paris (1958), pp. 148 ff.

11. *Ibid.:* "In spoken discourse inversion destroys *completely* all the sense and all the normal accepted value of the individual elements . . . inversion destroys the value of musical elements only in an infinitely weaker proportion: although the musical elements take on a strange character, they remain intelligible inasmuch as the articulation of the sequence of the sonorous objects remain perceptible . . . their aesthetic 'value' remains very close to what it was before."

10. Motion study.
Student photograph by M. Flint and F. Williams, M.I.T.

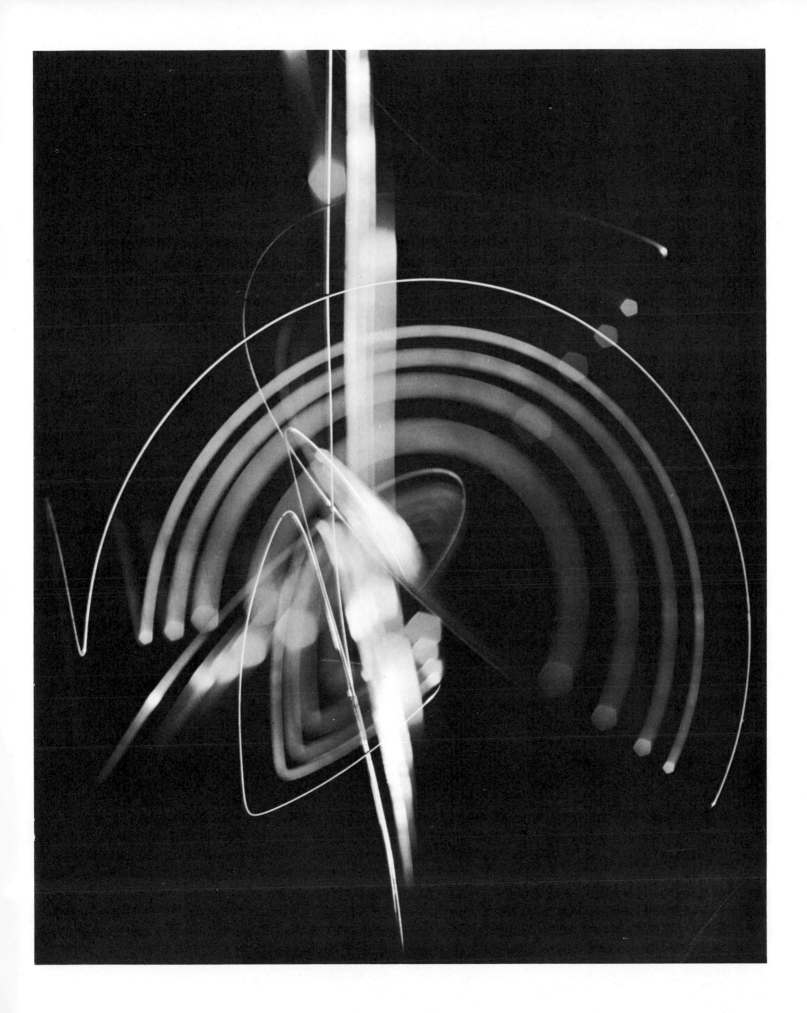

The farther natural science has developed the greater has been the discrepancy between the picture of the world which it has presented us and the world we experience through our senses. The physical world consists mostly of processes: molecules move and collide or they swing and rotate while forces hold them together; other dynamic processes make up chemical bonds; electrons move, revolve and spin, causing fields and all manner of radiation; nuclei are held together by mysterious forces, and at the other end of the scale, a living organism is an intricate array of a huge number of chemical processes. As opposed to this, the external world as we experience it through perception is mostly static. It consists mainly of forms and qualities. It is the qualitative nature of so many experiences that most strongly contrasts with the real nature of the physical world. All sorts of physical processes cause qualitative experiences in perception as, for instance, colors, tones, noises, the sensations of cold, warm and hot. The inner-organic processes also present themselves to the mind as qualities, like pain and other feelings. Even dynamic processes within the mind are often experienced in a qualitative manner as, for instance, yearning, frustration or mourning.

I suspect that, while it fascinates a few, this discrepancy in general helps to alienate the humanistically oriented individual from physical science. Yet the artist who fashions physical objects knows enough to be free of such an attitude. He realizes that to a large part the discrepancy is due to the medium of light, which connects our eyes with the physical objects we see. Some of the discrepancies, on the other hand, arise with the perceptual processes and this is why they interest us here. More often than is usually realized, our perceptual experience is influenced by the nature of the psychological processes that lead up to it. To be sure, much of this "creativity" serves to make perceptual experience truer than the intake of the eye would warrant: the tri-dimensionality of the environment, lost in the projection on the retina, is restored to visual experience, and correction is made for the effect of distance on projective size. An integrative process causes veridical form perception to emerge from a sequence of different views of an object, each of which by itself is insufficient to transmit all the information that serves to define the object's shape. Color perception is so organized that the lightness of the perceived colors is more in keeping with the reflectances of surfaces than with the light intensities which they happen to reflect under the prevailing illumination. But not all characteristics of perceptual experience that are due to the manner of operation of the perceptual processes serve to make perception more veridical than the conditions of stimulation which cause them. Some are simply peculiarities which are without any apparent sense and which happen to contribute toward the discrepancy between perceptual experience and our knowledge of the physical world. The term peculiarity may seem oddly disparaging, considering that I am talking about part of our primary reality, but I think it is used with justification.

One of the most interesting examples of such a peculiarity of perception is the manner in which we experience visual movement. There is an essential difference between motion as we experience it and motion as the physicist describes it. While to the physicist motion is primarily displacement of an object in relation to other objects—which object is displaced and which serves as a frame of reference is here merely a matter of description—visually perceived motion has no such relative aspect; it is felt to be entirely the affair of the moving object and may be described as a temporary attribute of that object. Even though we certainly can make ourselves aware of the displacement of a moving object in relation to other objects in the field, this awareness is by no means a genuine part of the perceived motion, which remains solely a property of the moving object.

It would be tempting to ascribe this discrepancy to the manner in which physical movements are represented in the stimulation that reaches the eye. Is not motion perceived when an object changes its position in relation to the observer, causing the eyes to pursue it? Since this need not involve another visual object, absence of a relative aspect from perceived motion would be in accord with the conditions of stimulation. Matters are, however, not so simple. Displacement of a visual object relative to the observer is not the only condition that leads to perception of motion, and is not even the most important one. Displacement of one object in the field of vision in relation to another one is also a cause of perceived motion. One may wonder how this effect could ever be demonstrated, since displacement of an object in relation to another object must always involve a displacement of at least one object with respect to the observer. The evidence comes from measurements of the threshold for movement under different conditions. Everybody is familiar with the fact that a physical movement may be too slow to lead to perceived motion. When an object that undergoes slow displacement is observed for an extended period, one may notice that it changes its position but the impression of motion may be absent. The objective velocity will have to be raised for experienced motion to emerge. The velocity at which this just barely happens is the threshold. It is fortunate that the threshold for motion is lower when an object moves in relation to another visual object than when it moves alone in the field of vision. In other words, in the presence of a stationary object a smaller velocity suffices to cause an impression of motion than when only the displacement between the moving object and the observer mediates the fact of movement. When, for example, in a completely dark room a single luminous dot is moved and observed, its velocity can be gradually reduced until the displacement is no longer perceived as motion. If then a second, stationary dot lights up near the moving one, motion will again be seen as long as the two dots do not move too far apart. Observations like this show that there are two different causes for the visual perception of motion. One condition of stimulation consists of the displacement of a seen object in relation to the observer; to this we shall refer with the term "angular displacement". The other condition of stimulation consists of the displacement of one object in relation to another object in the field of vision, henceforth called "object-relative displacement". The latter can be separately studied by using motion velocities below the threshold for angular displacement, the former by presenting the moving object in an otherwise homogeneous field.

Motion perceived on the basis of object-relative displacement alone presents an interesting question. Perceived motion, we have seen, consists in a specific attribute being temporarily inherent in an object; we call an object at rest when this attribute is absent. Thus, in experience, motion and rest are absolutes. When angular displacement is too slow to be effective, no information is imparted as to which of the objects in the visual field is actually displaced with respect to the observer. Therefore, we cannot expect that the object that moves relative to the observer will always be the one that is seen to move. This gives rise to the question: how will perceived motion and rest here distribute themselves among the objects that are being displaced relative to each other? When in an otherwise homogeneous visual field one object moves toward another object, either one, or even both, may be seen to move. The perceptual result of such an arrangement is as varied as its ambiguity would cause one to expect.

But when conditions of stimulation are so arranged that one of the two objects surrounds the other or forms its background, the resultant experience is always the same: the surrounded object is seen to move in a direction identical with that of its displacement in relation to its surround, and the surrounding pattern is seen at rest. This rule is rather strict and pervasive. Under ordinary circumstances, it would cause object-relative displacement to add its effect to that of angular displacement: an object that is being displaced in relation to the observer will also be displaced in relation to the stationary objects of the visual environment, and since the latter will usually form its surround it will be seen to move on object-relative grounds also.

But because of the rule, object-relative displacement may lead to illusory motion. This will happen to an object that is at rest relative to the observer while its surround is in motion. As the surrounded object it will still appear to move. We have here, in fact, the scheme of a well-known illusion of movement. It can be observed, for instance, when the moon is visible among drifting scattered clouds. The moon then appears to move in a direction opposite to that in which the clouds move. The clouds function here as the surrounding object and the moon as the surrounded one. Another example of this sort of illusory motion may be equally familiar to the reader: a pole standing in a steadily moving stream which carries along on its surface leaves or other debris; the pole appears to drift upstream.

This illusion, which is commonly called "induced movement", occurs because object-relative displacement prevails over angular displacement in causing experienced motion, where the two would tend to produce different effects. The pole, being stationary in relation to the observer, appears to move only on account of its displacement in relation to the surrounding pattern; that it does appear to move attests to the potency of object-relative displacement as a cause of perceived movement.

The very nature of object-relative displacement as a cue for motion perception has interesting consequences and leads to unexpected phenomena. Imagine, for instance, an arrangement of three figures inside each other: a small disk is surrounded by a larger outline square which, in turn, is surrounded by a still larger ring. Because they are projected, the ring and the square can be displaced

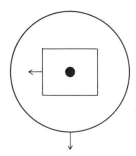

independently of each other. Objectively, the ring moves slowly downward, the square to the left and the disk is stationary. What movements will be perceived? Owing to angular displacement, the ring will be seen to move downward; the square, being displaced in relation to the ring obliquely upward and to the left, will be seen to move in that direction, and the disk will be seen to move to the right, for this is its displacement relative to the square.

That object-relative displacement is the more potent of the two conditions that cause perceived movement, becomes quite clear when the causes of motion speed are investigated. Speed is the attribute of perceived motion that we use in judging the velocity of physical motion, the impression of swiftness or slowness of movement. In 1927, J. F. Brown made a discovery which was at the time completely unexpected. For reasons which need not concern us here he had his subjects observe the speed of a small black disk that was seen moving through a bright aperture while the rest of the room was dark. There were, in fact, two such movement fields, with aperture and disk in one field twice the size of those in the other field. When the subjects compared speeds of the disks' motions and by changing the velocity in one of the fields made the speeds appear equal, it was found that the velocity in the larger field had to be almost twice as great as in the smaller field to produce such a speed match. The transposition phenomenon, as Brown called it, held for a wide range of velocities without a significant change in the velocity ratio that produced equal speeds. It was also possible to make the difference in the sizes of the movement fields much greater. For the very large size differences the ratio of matching velocities does not come as close to the ratio of the field sizes as it does for smaller differences, but the effect of field size on speed is still very great. This effect depends to a degree on dark room conditions. When the comparisons were made in daylight, the velocity ratios deviated more strongly from the size ratios. The explanation is undoubtedly that in daylight additional frames of references beyond the aperture edges become visible which are not transposed in size as the apertures are: the outer edges of the aperture frames, for instance, which happened to be equal in size. That this is the right explanation can be shown by covering the normally homogeneous aperture frames with identical patterns; this reduces the velocity ratio still further.

Today, the transposition phenomenon is readily understood. When perceived motion can result from displacement of an object in relation to another object, it is only sensible to expect that speed can depend on some property of object-relative displacement also. Let us for the moment assume that the transposition phenomenon occurs in ideal form, namely, that velocities have to be transposed in exactly the same ratio as the field sizes in order to produce equal speeds. Doubling both the size of the field and the velocity of the moving disk, for instance, would then leave the speed unchanged. The time that it takes a disk to traverse its aperture from end to end would also remain unchanged. Thus, rather simple relations result from the assumption of ideal transposition ratios. One might, for instance, say that speeds are equal when the objective displacement covers in unit time equal fractions of the aperture path. Speed would depend on the relative rate of displacement, where displacement is measured on a scale that depends on the size of the movement field in which it occurs. The transposition phenomenon may simply mean that, where motion is perceived on the basis of object-relative displacement, there is no general scale available in reference to which a rate of displacement could find definition. Instead, the distance that the moving object traverses in unit time is defined in terms of the scale of the movement field in which it takes place.

At this point it becomes necessary to talk briefly about the perception of form. The fact that we perceive form as such is probably the most important characteristic of visual perception, for the visual patterns that reach the eyes consist merely of an array of different brightnesses and colors. Having been part of our experience as far back as we can remember, form perception is so much taken for granted that few realize that it is the product of the perceptual processes, rather than directly given in the visual input. Yet the fact that it is possible to render some essential properties of a scene by means of an outline drawing should make this evident. All the primary data of color and shading are here eliminated, and by means of a single differentiation in brightness an experience of form is transmitted which is often equivalent to that produced by viewing the natural scene. An outline drawing directly establishes an experience that organizing processes, in the presence of a natural environment, extract from the given color pattern.

The fact that form as we experience it is not directly given in visual stimulation, but is rather a product of the mind, has many interesting consequences. Most widely known of these is the ambiguity of plane patterns, which is connected with the reversibility of figure and ground. One of the properties of form that is relevant to our discussion of motion is the fact that a visual pattern can be changed in size without changing the form which it causes in experience. Form perception may have a bearing on the perception of motion because the displacement of an object relative to its surround can be regarded as a change in the form that the object and its surround taken together make up. The motion of our disk through its aperture offers a simple example. Disk and aperture edge together show different forms dependent on the various positions that the disk passes on its movement through the aperture. Object-relative displacement may thus be taken to mean form change, and inasmuch as form is not affected by change in size, proportionate displacements in transposed movement fields would represent identical form changes. Thus, when the velocities of the disks are in the same proportion as the corresponding field sizes, the displacements produce form changes at equal rates, and this is most probably the reason why they tend to produce equal speed. The fact that in Brown's experiments the results merely approach the ideal proportionate values is easily understood. Brown had his disks move with velocities which made their motion effective through their angular displacement also, and to the degree to which speed depends on angular displacement it should be expected to approach veridicality. We shall return to this point later.

The interpretation of object-relative displacement as form change, which explains the transposition principle, is further supported by an entirely different fact. This fact is related to another property of form perception: the strange dependence of experienced form on the orientation of the given pattern relative to the upright of the visual field. Tipping a square by 45 degrees leaves its shape geometrically unaltered but its perceived form changed; it will look so different that it commands a different word in the English language. It can be shown that this dependence of form on orientation is reflected in motion perception.

When two bright dots in an otherwise dark field are displaced in the same direction and at the same rate, no motion will be seen if the velocity is below the threshold for angular displacement, for the distance between the dots does not change and no object-relative displacement occurs. There is still another way to displace two points so that the distance between them is not changed: to have them revolve about each other, or simpler yet, to have one point move about the other on a circular path. This arrangement, however, involves a change in orientation. The pair of points, being related to each other in experience, produces in every position it assumes a different impression of direction. If change in orientation is equivalent to object-relative displacement, motion should be perceived even when the velocity of the point on the circular path is slowed below the threshold for angular displacement, and this is indeed the case. A mere change in orientation of a rigid pattern causes perceived motion at the slow rate at which object-relative displacement alone is normally effective. Only the notion that perceived movement depends on form change offers an explanation of this fact.

Strong evidence, then, argues that movement perceived on grounds of object-relative displacement is mediated by form perception and is based on form change. Two properties of form perception —the invariance of form under transformation in size, and the dependence of form on orientation— were found to be characteristics of motion perception also.

The realization that one of the two conditions of stimulation for motion leads to perceived movement by way of form perception makes the next question to be taken up only more interesting: what exactly is the relation between the two conditions, angular displacement and object-relative displacement? There are two facts that throw light on the matter.

The first of these has to do with Brown's transposition phenomenon. The experiments that yielded this finding are interesting in still another way: they cause the two conditions of stimulation to be in conflict with each other. With the two movement fields at equal distances from the observer, angular displacement by itself should yield veridical speeds, that is, speeds should appear to be equal when the objective velocities are the same. If, on the other hand, the speed of perceived motion depended merely on the rate of form change, speeds in the transposed movement fields should appear matched when the velocities are exactly in the same proportion as the field sizes. The actual results obtained are the outcome of both conditions of stimulation taking effect simultaneously, and can serve as an indication of the relative effectiveness of the two conditions. The fact that the velocity ratios approach those of the field sizes and are far from being veridical indicates a preponderance of the effect of object-relative displacement.

The other fact that is relevant here leads to more striking conclusions. Numerous arrangements of objective movement are known where a given displacement leads to two perceived movements seen simultaneously. In every case, one of the two perceived movements results from that component of the actual displacement which is given through an object-relative displacement, while the other perceived movement corresponds to what remains of the actual displacement after that component has been subtracted. We shall discuss two specific examples.

The first example, although somewhat complicated, is presented because it has received much attention in the past. A wheel rolls on a horizontal rail in the dark. A small point of light is fixed to the face of the wheel near its rim and is the only object visible. Its objective motion will describe a well-known curve of successive arches, called cycloid, which results from vectorial addition of two simple

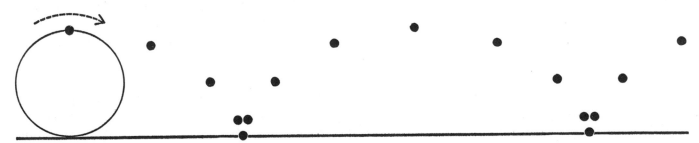

motion paths, a circular one produced by a point revolving about a center, the wheel's hub, and a straight one, of the translatory motion of the wheel as a whole. The observer perceives the situation as it is, motion through a path of repeated arches. But when a second point of light is added near the wheel's rim diametrically across from the first, the arch-shaped motion paths will cease to be seen. Instead the two light points will appear to revolve about each other and in addition to move together on a straight horizontal path. For each light point the actual cycloid path is now broken down into the two mentioned components. Why does this happen? It has been argued that revolution of the two points about each other plus a translatory motion of the pair is a simpler process than the alternative one where two arch-shaped motion paths penetrate each other. But there is a less speculative interpretation possible: the revolution of the two points about each other is given by object-relative displacement, while the translatory motion of the pair is given by angular displacement alone. If the objective movements were slowed down below the threshold of an effective angular displacement, only the revolution would be seen (even if cycloid motion had been perceived at higher velocities).

Our other example is one from a number of further instances of simultaneously perceived movements which were discovered by Gunnar Johansson. Here two dark spots on a light background moved in straight lines, one vertically downward and the other horizontally to the left so that their movement converged on a point, and then they returned over the same paths to the starting positions. Thus the combined motion paths formed an L. The observer invariably saw the two spots move straight toward each other on an oblique path until they met and then back on the same slant. At the same time they also seemed to move as a group obliquely down to the left and then back up to the right. Of the two simultaneous motions, the movement of the spots toward and away from each other was much more conspicuous. In fact, only about 65 per cent of the observers reported the second motion spontaneously; the others had to be questioned and then "confirmed its presence without hesitation."

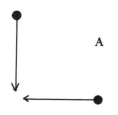
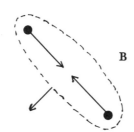

A shows the actual motion paths in Johansson's experiment. B shows the experienced motion.

It is easy to see what goes on here. Each spot's motion path gives rise to two component movements. One motion of each spot is along the line connecting their extreme end positions; the other is at right angles to this line. The first results from the displacement of the spots in relation to each other, in which they approach each other, overlap for a moment and recede again. The second corresponds to the residual component of the motion path which is effective as a displacement relative to the observer only. By no stretch of the imagination can it be argued that the separation into two component movements results here in a simpler process. On the contrary, single motion of each spot corresponding to its objective horizontal or vertical displacement would be by far simpler. Only one explanation makes sense here: the oblique motion of the spots toward and away from each other is given through

58

object-relative displacement (and would be the only motion seen if velocities were slowed down to the point where angular displacement is ineffective); the other corresponds to the residual angular displacement.

This explanation fits all instances where objects are seen to undergo two movements simultaneously. If it is accepted, these instances show a striking prevalence of motion based on object-relative displacement over motion based on angular displacement. In such instances object-relative displacement comprises only part of the total displacement, whereas angular displacement represents the displacement in its entirety. Thus, neither one of the two perceived motions corresponds to the total angular displacement, while one does correspond to the object-relative displacement. The perceptual process based on the latter pre-empts, so to speak, the given displacement and the second perceived motion corresponds to the residual displacement. The motion process that is caused by object-relative displacement is truly predominant.

Little is known about the manner in which angular displacement leads to perceived motion, and this is probably the reason why there is at this time no further light on the relationship between the two conditions of stimulation that give rise to perceived motion. Allowing ourselves some speculation, we might be inclined to ascribe the fact that motion is perceived as an attribute of a moving object, rather than a relative displacement, to the existence of angular displacement as an effective condition of stimulation. Angular displacement is relative only in respect to the viewer himself; as a visual object the moving thing is unique. And since there can be little doubt that angular displacement appeals to a phylogenetically older perceptual mechanism, the idea that angular displacement is responsible for the peculiar way we perceive motion has a certain force.

On the other hand, that motion is perceived as a temporary attribute of an object is in keeping also with the way object-relative displacement operates. As we have seen, object-relative displacement takes effect by the route of form perception. There is a parallelism in form perception to the peculiar manner in which relative displacement is treated in motion perception, namely, the phenomenon of figure and ground. Of two areas of different color, one surrounding the other, the surrounded area is usually seen as figure; that is, the border-line between the two areas becomes the surrounded area's boundary, limits it, and gives it shape, while the surrounding area does not appear to be bounded by that border-line, derives no shape from it, becomes ground. Similarly, in a relative displacement between an object and the surrounding pattern, the surrounded object attains the attribute of motion, and the surround is perceived at rest. Both phenomena are arbitrary as far as the conditions of stimulation are concerned and reflect the creative nature of our most basic perceptual process.

JAMES J. GIBSON
CONSTANCY AND INVARIANCE IN PERCEPTION

Why do things look as they do? Why do they appear, on the whole, pretty much as they are? The makers of things-to-be-seen need to understand how we see. So also, for that matter, do the *consumers* of things-to-be-seen—those of us who enjoy looking at artifacts of any sort, particularly at pictures. Perceiving for its own sake—contemplating, registering, detecting, discriminating, and comprehending—is not only a pleasure, it is useful. It can even be thought of as a sort of discipline. Artists have long believed that in making "art" they learn to perceive "nature", and that they can thereby show the rest of us how to see it better. Artists are bound to be psychologists insofar as they are concerned with the psychological question of how a perceiver does what he does. By the same token the perception-psychologist ought to be concerned with art.

The psychology of perception, however, is a large field with a long history, a bewildering series of controversies, and a vast amount of evidence on both sides of the issues. It includes the study of the physiology of sensations at one extreme, and the philosophy of knowledge at the other. A bare introduction to the subject is given in a long and difficult book by E. G. Boring entitled *Sensation and Perception in the History of Experimental Psychology*.[1] Any artist who even attempts to read everything important that has been written about it is a bold man. Gombrich has recently done so in his study of the psychology of pictorial representation.[2] Although he found the literature illuminating, he also found it full of contradictions.

The central puzzle of perception, I believe, is the problem of what is called constancy. This term is not very familiar outside of psychology, and I shall try to explain what the term means and why it is considered so important.

Constancy is the tendency to perceive an object as the same despite changing sense-impressions. One sees the size of an object fairly well at quite different distances from the eye. One sees the shape of the face of an object correctly even when it is slanted or inclined to the line of sight, i.e., foreshortened. The impression of "extent" changes with distance and the impression of "form" changes with inclination, but the perception, on the whole, does not. Likewise both the perception of surface-color and of white-black do not seem to vary much with the color and intensity of the light entering the eye (which change with varying illumination, or shadows) but depend on a property of the surface—the differential absorbing and reflecting of incident light. These three facts are called size constancy, shape constancy, and color constancy, and a great number of experiments have been carried out in psychological laboratories to discover the conditions under which they occur, to measure the tendencies, and to test the theories which purport to explain them. It is fair to say that these facts are as much a puzzle now as they were half a century ago when they began to be studied.

The constancies of size, shape, and color are not the whole of the matter. It is becoming clear that there is a much larger set of constancies in perception, not so easily labelled. All of them involve a discrepancy between the sense impression and the experience of the ordinary naïve observer. Some of these are worth describing, in order to show the scope of the problem.

Constancy of perceived space. Not only is the size of a single rigid body seen to be the same at different distances and the shape the same from different viewpoints, but also the size and shape of two bodies in different places can be compared. Their dimensions and proportions are visible. Moreover, the apparent distances between bodies, as well as the objects themselves, remain constant. One can match the separation of two things which are far off with two things nearby. Similarly, one can say whether the edges of a road running off into the distance (or two stretched strings controlled by an experimenter) are parallel or not. What remains constant in such situations is the scale of things and the intervals between things. It is the ground, not just the bodies resting on the ground, that keeps the same size and shape in experience.

One can put these facts in another way by saying that what men are conscious of are the surfaces of their environment, and the *layout* of these surfaces. So far as the evidence goes, this also holds true for children and, on behavioral evidence, for animals. Observers are not ordinarily conscious of the patchwork of colors in the field of view as this is determined by the laws of perspective. Instead they perceive the environing surfaces with their edges, corners, slants, convexities, concavities, and interspaces. These are, of course, the pathways and obstacles, the places and things, the goals and the dangers of the terrestrial world. They are identified by their surface properties, including texture and differential reflectance of light. They have to be seen as constant, where they are, in order to be identified for what they are.

Historically, the central problem of perception has been taken to be how we see depth and distance, the so-called third dimension of space. The psychologist and the painter have been led to ask what the clues or cues may be for tridimensional perception as distinguished from bidimensional sensation. It begins to be evident, however, that the heart of the problem is not so much how we see objects in depth as how we see the constant layout of the world around us. Space as such, empty space, is not visible but surfaces are.

The apparent rigidity of the phenomenal world. Whenever an observer moves from place to place, the pattern of his field of view—that is, the optic array that determines his retinal image[3]—undergoes a perspective transformation. This follows, of course, from the facts of perspective at a stationary point. There is a deformation of this array as a whole and in every part. The visual sense-impression, therefore, changes with every change of position. Unless an observer holds his head unnaturally still and fixes his eye, his visual field is alive with transformation. A sensation of "form", then, is an extreme rarity in life; what normally stimulates the eye is a continuous transformation in time. Nevertheless perception is of rigid things, of a rigid ground, and of constant separations between fixed things. The phenomenal world is not distorted during locomotion, although it ought to be if perception is based on sensation.

The same perspective transformation of the field that occurs when the head is moved from right to left appears simultaneously in one eye relative to the other when both eyes are open. This disparity of the two fields, the mismatch of pattern, yields a sensation called double imagery. But perception is not doubled and the mismatch can only be noticed if a man attends to his subjective sense-impressions instead of to the world.

Other discrepancies between sensation and perception. The set of color-patches which make up the visual field continually change in a jerky fashion as the eyes scan the array of ambient light. We move our eyes from one fixation point to another several times a second during waking life. We also blink frequently. The sense impressions, therefore, are highly unstable and interrupted. But an obvious

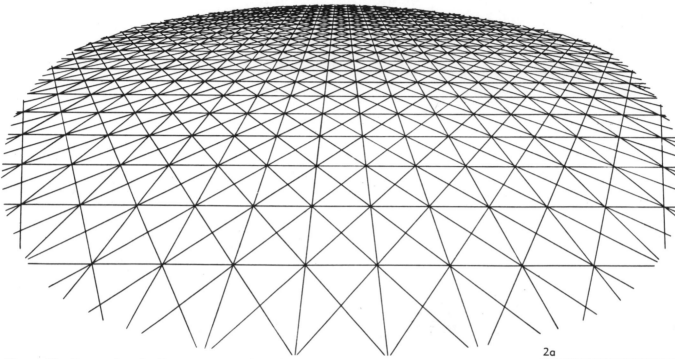

Fig. 1. *The Perspective of a Pavement*. Note that when this picture is observed from the proper station-point the ground tends to emerge in experience, not so the visual sensations. The blocks appear equal in size, the same in shape, with edges parallel. They recede into the distance instead of getting smaller or denser. The scale remains constant. The space is Euclidean. (From Gibson, *Perception of the Visual World,* Houghton Mifflin, 1950)

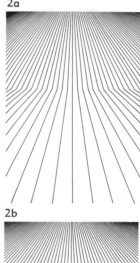

2a

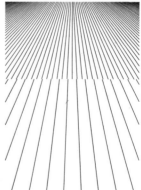

2b

Fig. 2a. *The Visual Stimulus for a Corner*. Whenever the gradient of density in an optic array abruptly changes rate in this manner one sees a "corner", i.e., two adjoining surfaces at an angle. This one is concave. The mathematical information would be the same for any other texture. It is an invariant piece of information in the light to a station-point.

Fig. 2b. *The Visual Stimulus for an Edge*. Whenever the gradient of density in an optic array abruptly changes *density* in this manner, one sees an "edge" with depth behind it, i.e., a step downward, a falling-off place. This mathematical discontinuity is also an invariant. It carries external meaning —important meaning for anyone walking toward the edge. (From Gibson, *Perception of the Visual World*)

characteristic of perception is its stability and continuity. The world does not seem to move as the retinal image moves over the retina. Here is another sort of constancy.

Human visual sensation is clear only in the center of the field corresponding to the central fovea of the eye at each momentary fixation. It is a fleeting impression. But visual perception, being extended over time and depending on the whole array of ambient light, may be clear in all directions. The momentary sensation is bounded by the margins of the cone of light rays that can enter the eye. But visual perception is unbounded. We are aware of a world that surrounds us like a panorama, not a cone of rays. I have described these contrasts more fully in Chapter 3 of *The Perception of the Visual World*.[4)]

Constancy in perception other than visual. The stability of perception with unstable sensations holds true for all the receptive systems, not only the visual system. Just as the visible world does not seem to rotate 90° when one lies down on his side, although the retinal image does, so the tangible ground and the direction of gravity do not seem to swing upward, although the tactual impression has shifted from one's feet to one's flank and the weights in the sacs of the inner ear now pull sideways to the head. Instead of the ground changing, one feels that *he* has changed and the earth has not.

Sensations of touch are often radically different from perceptions of touch. One gets a tactual impression whenever the skin is pushed in, usually by contact with a solid body. But when one touches an object with the fingers he feels the object, not the contacts. When you move your groping fingers over an unfamiliar object with eyes closed you will experience its shape, size, proportions, and rigidity but you will be almost wholly unaware of the sequence of cutaneous impressions. The same single object, a pencil for example, is felt whether you hold it with two, three, four, or five fingers, and this means with two, three, four, or five different sensations at different places on the skin. In short the perception is unitary despite diversity of the impressions. When you press on a surface lightly or heavily you do not feel the changing intensity of the impression; you feel only the unchanging solidity of the object. When you move your hand over the edges and corners of a rigid body, you do not feel the cutaneous motion over the skin; you feel a motionless object with a moving hand. The perception is constant and stable although the sensations are changing and mobile.

The channels for stimulus information that we have arbitrarily separated and called "senses" are normally active and exploratory, not passive and receptive. It begins to be clear, I think, that the passive arousal of sensations, as these have been studied by sensory physiologists, is not typical of the way perception works in life.

One more example may be offered, from hearing. The sensory qualities of auditory experience are said to be loudness, pitch, and tonal complexity. A great deal is known about the corresponding variables of physical sound. But the perceptions arising in auditory experience are of outer happenings, inanimate events, cries, and the speech of our fellow men. The perceiving of speech sounds is largely independent of loudness, pitch, and tonal complexity. The proof is that we hear the same speech whether it is whispered or shouted, voiced or sung, produced by male or female vocal organs. The critical speech sounds, the phonemes, depend on properties of sound that are invariant, that is, properties which do not change when the level of intensity or the level of pitch is altered.

Theories of the invariance of perception with varying sensations. How can the experience of a constant world arise from the ever changing flux of sensory impressions? This is the central puzzle. If the data of sense vary, how can the perception of unvarying places and things be explained? The constancies of size, shape, and color of objects together with all the other sorts of constancy are the principal reason for theories of perception.

Theories of perception go back for hundreds of years and have occupied the best efforts of some of the greatest thinkers in history. They cannot be here summarized, but they can be classified roughly. They seem to fall into three types: first, those that appeal to innate ideas or the rational faculties of the mind for making the sensory data intelligible; second, those that appeal to past experience, memory, or learning for supplementing and interpreting the sensory data; and third, a recent theory which asserts that the sensory chaos is organized by a spontaneous process of self-distribution in the brain.

It should be noted that all these theories assume without question that sense impressions are somehow the cause of perception but not a sufficient cause. They are taken to be the occasion for perception, the basis for it, or the raw material from which perception is constructed. These theories all take for granted the poverty of the senses and seek for a special process in the mind or the brain to supplement them. They assume that the organs of sense are passive, or merely receptive, accepting whatever physical stimulation enters as if they were merely windows. The activity of perception is supposed to be an internal or subjective process. Meaning is supposed to come from inside, not from outside. These assumptions, as will appear later, can be challenged. It might be that no special process is necessary to explain perception, and that in fact perception is not based on sensation. But this is getting ahead of the story.

The theory of innate ideas and faculties. It is possible to suppose that perceiving, although occasioned by having sensations, is chiefly a matter of intuition. The idea of a constant and fixed Euclidean space, for example, may be simply a part of the inborn capacity of the human mind. The continually changing perspectives of visual sensation are interpreted in terms of this abstract concept as rigid objects. But the mind is informed by its own preconceptions, not by the sense impressions.

The theory of the accumulation of past experience. By far the most popular theory of perception is that of empiricism, as contrasted with nativism. Concepts and general ideas are taken to be learned, not inborn. They are the residue of all the fleeting perspectives of the past. We have learned that objects are constant in shape and size and color and therefore we unwittingly interpret our sensations in accordance with what we have learned about objects. According to Helmholtz, the process is one of "unconscious inference", the sense data serving only as clues to the real nature of the objects.

This explanation, or one of its many variants, is so widely accepted that many people have never heard of any other. It has the virtue of emphasizing training or learning instead of the mysterious faculties of the mind. It allows for the possibility of the improvement of our perceptual abilities with the accumulation of memories. But as an explanation it is weak and it was destructively criticized a generation ago by the proponents of another theory, especially by Koffka.[5]

The theory of sensory organization. Gestalt theory. Koffka asked how a perceiver could be supposed to learn about objects if all he had to go on were the flux of meaningless sensations. How could a child learn to see an object without ever seeing one? A theory of association, or of the learning of clues, cannot explain it unless the objectivity of an object is given at some time. There was evidence to suggest, moreover, that inexperienced animals and children did not behave as if they confused a large far object with a near small object—in short that they did not see their retinal images in the first place.

The *Gestalt* theorists proposed that a process of sensory organization instead of association was the explanation of perception. The nature of the nervous system is such that organization takes place spontaneously. Experience is structured; it comes in a field and, at the very least, there is always a "figure" on a "ground". It is never wholly meaningless, even at the start.

Koffka also made the acute observation that, in perceiving an object, we do not separately see a retinal size and then a distance, or a retinal shape and then a slant; instead we see all at once a size-at-a-distance, or a shape-at-a-slant. The relationship between the members of these pairs is invariant in experience, he noted, the visual angle for a given object being reciprocal to distance and the perspective flattening being concomitant with slant. Form and space are linked together, as it were, not separable. It is only a step from this idea to the hypothesis that a shape-at-a-slant may actually be given as an invariant within two variables of optical stimulation, although this is a step that Koffka did not take.

The *Principles of Gestalt Psychology*[5] was certainly the most knowledgeable book on visual perception ever written, and it is still a good foundation for new knowledge. *Gestalt* theory has been called a modern form of nativism and there is a grain of truth in this observation, for the hypothetical "laws of visual organization" bear some analogy to innate forms of apprehension. But the trend or direction of the theory was novel and its emphasis on structure, order, articulation, pattern, and the "total field" of perception is still to be followed up. The proposed laws of organization have not been verified experimentally. But some kind of organization in perception is a fact. The question is where it comes from. Perhaps it comes from outside, not inside.

The relation between stimuli and their sources in the environment. It was only in the era of *Gestalt* theory that the paradox of perceptual constancy became clear, although it has been the root of the difficulty all along. In my terminology, it is the invariance of perception with varying sensations. The other side of the problem is, the invariance of physical objects with what seem to be varying physical stimuli.

One must not confuse the stimuli for the eyes, the ears, and the skin with the sources of these stimuli in the environment. The light, the sound, and the mechanical energy respectively must be distinguished from the objects that reflect light, emit sound, or come in contact with the skin. The impinging physical energy is called the *proximal* stimulus, the stimulus proper, and the external object or event is called the *distal* or *distant* stimulus. The sense organs are excited only by proximal stimuli but what the perceiver is aware of are distal stimuli. This is the other side of the paradox of perceptual constancy. The environment is constant, the stimuli are changing, the sensations are changing, and the perception is constant. The distance, depth, solidity, and permanence of the environment seem to be lost in the proximal stimuli and in the sensory impressions but they turn up again, almost miracu-

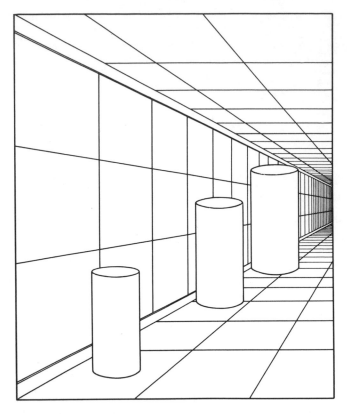

Fig. 3. *The Reciprocity of Size and Distance.* The pictorial sizes of the images of the cylinders in this drawing are equal, but the phenomenal sizes of the virtual cylinders in the space of the picture are different, the farthest being two and a half times larger than the nearest. One sees the size-at-a-distance, not the sensation of size. The distance of each cylinder is given by its place in the gradient of texture. The size of each cylinder is given by the number of texture elements it intercepts. The size of an object depends on the scale of the space where it is and this tends to remain constant even in pictorially represented space.

(From Gibson, *Perception of the Visual World*)

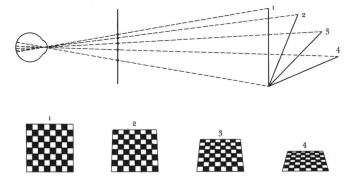

Fig. 4. *The Reciprocity of Shape and Slant.* The phenomenal shape of a checkerboard remains constant despite change of slant. One tends to see the square at a slant, not the trapezoidal sensation. One explanation is that the impression of trapezoidal shape is corrected or compensated by the clues for slant. But a simpler explanation would be that the information for both the shape and the slant of the surface is given by the texture. The surface-shape is what counts, not the ghost-shape of its projected edges.

(From Gibson, *Perception of the Visual World*)

lously, in perception. The third dimension of space is said to be lost in the two-dimensional visual image but restored by some activity of the mind (or the memory, or the brain) in visual experience.

The study of the senses has always involved the study of proximal stimuli, and experimenters have been applying energies to the sense organs of their subjects to see what happens for more than a century. A great deal more is now known about stimuli than when the theories were first formulated. It used to be thought that they were bits of energy, points and movements. But the evidence accumulates that the field of stimulation and the flow of stimulation are what is important in arousing sense organs. Both the field and the flow must have a pattern or structure. What excites the eye, for example, is not an even distribution of light but at least one contrast or margin; and not a fixed level of intensity but a change. The effective stimuli are gradients and transients, and this is as true for the ear and the skin as it is for the eye.

It used to be thought that stimuli could not possibly represent their sources in the world. Objects do not get into the eye; only light can enter. It is true that an object cannot be *replicated* in light rays, but the properties of its surface can be *specified* by them. Perspective carries some information about the object, and change of perspective carries still more.[6] An observer who has "looked at all sides of a thing" is one who has sensed it in all possible perspectives. As he moves around it his eyes are stimulated by a whole family of serial transformations. The perspective forms change from moment to moment, but note that they change in perfectly orderly and in completely reversible ways. It has been taken for granted that the ever changing form of the stimulus is a chaos which cannot possibly contain the solid form of the object. But perhaps it can. The true shape of the object may be implicit in the serial transformations. In that case, order does not have to be imposed on the momentary stimuli; it is already there in the sequential stimulus.

The relation between orderly stimuli and their sources, then, may not be as tenuous as we have thought in the past. The varying stimuli which go with unvarying objects in the world may have an unvarying component. And this leads us back to the theory of perception.

A new approach to the invariance of perception. I have a suspicion that the theories of perception have been on the wrong track. It has often been true in the history of thought that a puzzling problem cannot be solved but has to be reformulated, and perhaps this is true of the problem of constancy.

The invariance of perception with varying sensations ought to lead to the conclusion that sensations do not cause perceptions. But that seems to go against common sense, for we perceive only when the sense organs are stimulated—otherwise we only imagine or remember or guess the facts of the world. The way out may be this: that sensory experience is a special self-conscious kind of awareness while perceptual experience is unselfconscious and direct. The latter does not depend on the former. Perception is not mediated by sensations, nor based on sensations.

This requires that the stimuli causing sensations be different from those causing perceptions. This is a new idea, not at all evident but very promising when it is considered. The individual is bathed in a sea of energy at all times, and the stimulus energies that his receptors can pick up are a flowing array. Light, sound, and physical touchings are patterned, both simultaneously and successively. The hypothesis is that the flowing array has two components, one of change and one of non-change.

This hypothesis can be sharpened by borrowing from mathematics two notions. One is that of *transformations* and the other is that of *invariants under transformation*. These terms, although not taught us in beginning geometry, are fundamental. They are much more useful than the notion of "form" as the Greeks conceived it.[7] Stimuli are not static forms but serial transformations which are nevertheless lawful. A static form is simply a special case of continued non-transformation. Transformation, in mathematics, is not simply change but permanence in change. The specific hypothesis is that the invariant component in a transformation carries information about an object and that the variant component carries other information entirely, for example, about the relation of the perceiver to the object. When an observer attends to certain invariants he perceives objects; when he attends to certain variants he has sensations.

This hypothesis is incomplete (and probably the same thing can be said in another way) but it explains the constancy of objective perception without recourse to theories of a subjective process. It also explains how perception can be, in effect, focused on the sources of stimulation, although it is in fact wholly dependent on the stimulation itself. For the permanent properties of the outer world—its texture, edges, layout, solidity, stability, and the fact of gravity—are undoubtedly specified by invariant properties in the visual and tactual stimulus flux. We can thus understand why perceiving is so often correct without recourse to difficult philosophical theories.

Extra hypotheses are needed about what I have called the variant component of stimulus transformation. They are speculative, and need investigation. For one thing, we must suppose that there is a difference between perspective transformations and other transformations. In vision, a perspective transformation results from a movement of the object relative to the observer or of the observer relative to the object. But if the thing observed is fluid or viscous or ephemeral or changeable in itself, not simply moveable, a quite different sort of transformation occurs in the light to the eye. The difference is quite noticeable.[8] If the thing observed is broken or disrupted still another transformation occurs, a permutation of order in the stimulus, and the event is visible as such.

Another extra hypothesis is needed about self-produced transformations of the stimulus-array as contrasted with those not dependent on action of one's own. In moving one's eyes, or head, or body, or in manipulating external objects, one changes the optical stimulus array in whole or part. Each action has its own family of transformations, and each is accompanied by a family of other feelings. We can thus control our responses and explore the possibilities of new stimulation. Locomotion, for example, is guided in this way. We even hear our own footsteps. But some changes in the pattern of light or touch or sound are not self-produced in this circular fashion. They are object-produced. The absence of circularity may well be the feature of these stimuli that gives the corresponding perceptions their external reference. A clue to the whole muddle of explaining how experience can be both external and internal, both objective and subjective, may lie here.

Still another hypothesis is needed about the way in which perception develops in the child, and how discrimination improves in the adult. Presumably it is a matter of the growth and the education of attention. The theory that the infant has only meaningless sensations based on raw stimuli and later enriches these impressions with memories is not good enough. The child learns, but what he probably learns is to fix on the subtle variables of stimulation instead of only the crude ones. He does not have to construct a constant world out of ever changing perspectives but he does have to discover the finer properties of the world that lie hidden in these transformations.

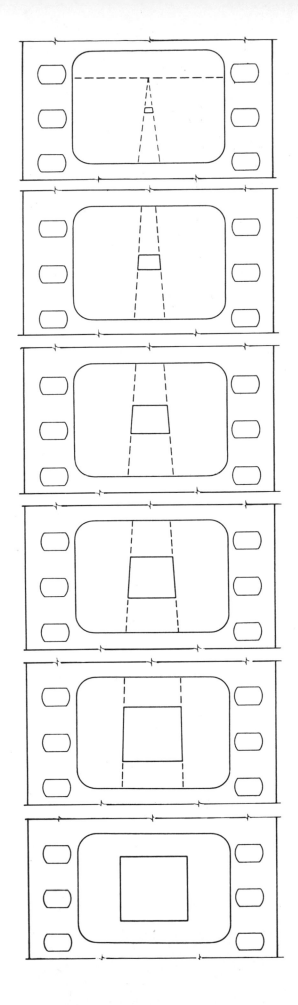

Fig. 5. *A Serial Transformation.* This sequence, from top to bottom, shows the perspective transformation of the projection of a unit of pavement as one walks closer to it. We are accustomed to think that the form changes over time, but we forget that certain important properties of the form do not change; the permanence is just as important for our perception as the change. The transformation specifies approach. The invariant under transformation specifies the constant object. (From *Perception of the Visual World*)

1. E. G. Boring, *Sensation and Perception in the History of Experimental Psychology*, New York, Appleton-Century-Crofts (1942).

2. E. H. Gombrich, *Art and Illusion: A Study in the Psychology of Pictorial Representation*, New York, Pantheon (1960).

3. J. J. Gibson, "Ecological optics," in *Vision Research* (1:1961), pp. 253–262.

4. J. J. Gibson, *The Perception of the Visual World*, Boston, Houghton Mifflin (1950).

5. K. Koffka, *Principles of Gestalt Psychology*, New York, Harcourt Brace (1935).

6. J. J. Gibson, *The Perception of the Visual World*, Ch. 7.

7. J. J. Gibson, "What is a form?," in *Psychological Review* (58:1951), pp. 403–412; idem., "Optical motions and transformations as stimuli for visual perception," in *Psychological Review* (64:1957), pp. 288–295.

8. K. von Fieandt and J. J. Gibson, "The sensitivity of the eye to two kinds of continuous transformation of a shadow-pattern," in *Journal of Experimental Psychology* (57:1959), pp. 344–347.

STANLEY W. HAYTER

ORIENTATION, DIRECTION, CHEIRALITY, VELOCITY AND RHYTHM

Most of the literature on the arts has to do not only with things that cannot be described but even with things that cannot be known. Although it is quite possible to describe the operations which result in a work of art and furthermore to describe the effect on the spectator of the work when it is complete, what happens between the artist and his work cannot be clearly known or described in words even by the artist himself. Any attempt to do this results in a sort of literary game of words about words and brings us no nearer to an understanding of the matter. However, the techniques of projection —not only the mechanical means through which an image appears, but the attitude of mind and the conscious direction of the thought of the artist—are well worth investigating.

Once an effective communication has been arrived at the analysis of the result becomes possible. Of this character *Point, Line to Space* of Kandinsky and *Pedagogical Sketchbook* of Klee are quite typical and arise not only from the practice of art but also from the teaching of art, which involves explanation and justification of the means used. Some of the suggestions which follow come from the author's experience over the last thirty years of teaching, or rather of working in collaboration with a group of international artists; these associates have certainly no less equipment, intelligence and imagination than himself.

The logical method of exposition will be followed here, solely because this is clearly and universally understood even if the matter itself is not always rational; the logical exposition of irrational matter has become familiar to us in recent psychology. The matter of this paper deals with the *means,* not the ends or the incentives. The author's theory of technique (i.e., that awareness of means should stimulate areas of imagination not otherwise accessible) will not be discussed here.

The somewhat elaborate title of this paper, originally intended to describe the equivalents of motion in graphic expression, became necessary when it was realized that all of these elements were involved in any discussion of motion. Thus *orientation* signifies direction only with regard to the position of the spectator (where he is); *direction,* as north-going or south-going (where he goes); *cheirality,* right- or left-handedness; *velocity,* how far in how long; and *rhythm,* the continued sense of how often. It may not be clear immediately that all of these terms except for the first involve the consideration

of time. In this study I shall attempt to proceed from a partial demonstration with the intention of amplifying the treatment progressively to include all of the operative factors.

If an observer can only see in a plane, he can observe a line but not an area. If he can place himself above or below the plane he can observe an area. If he needs to observe a volume in depth, he must be free to move, or there must be movement in the object he is observing. That is to say, if there are two poles exactly in line, in order to decide which one is the nearer either the observer must move (though the movement of his two eyes may also be sufficient), or one or other of the poles must be moving. Thus in order to perceive this depth, an element of time, which is involved with movement, is necessary. This element of time proceeds in our ordinary experience in one direction only; that is, it is not symmetrical as if it proceeded in either direction. In any figuration in our field of vision the possibilities of motion can be no less than two: 1) the actual displacement of the object; 2) the displacement of the eye or of the person. The latter occurs when the dimensions are greater than the maximum visual angle. We all know that for one seated in a train in motion, or seated in a train not in motion and looking at another train in motion, the two experiences are the same and indistinguishable. That is, as far as our experience goes, it does not matter whether our train moves, the other train moves or both are moving at different speeds: the experience of motion is that of a difference in velocities.

Thus the equivalent of motion in graphic terms becomes the motion of the eye of the observer, or when the scale is sufficiently great, his actual displacement. In view of the principle just cited, however, such motion on the part of the observer is as real as motion in the object itself, since the sensation by which it is perceived is undistinguishable from the sensation of witnessing independent motion.

The first step in understanding the factors of motion is to investigate that field of vision in which it is seen. For the purpose of this study, we will restrict this field to that which subtends about twenty degrees of visual angle, equivalent to the average field perceived without movement. For most people any wider field involves a series of observations with actual movement of the head. The vertical extent of the field is normally somewhat less. Although it is possible to observe this area (about

150 cms. x 100 cms. at six meters' distance) in a single glance, actual experiment nonetheless shows a motion in the eye of the observer.

In a series of experiments made at the New School in 1940 and 1941 (results not published as far as I know), it was found that, in scanning a field, without exception the motion of the eye was from left to right (W. to E.). And this was true even in the case of left-handed subjects, and Orientals whose habit of reading was right to left or from top downwards. In the same experiments it was found that the diagonal in a rectangle, from lower left to upper right (S.W. to N.E.), was read in an upward direction, while the mirror image of this diagonal, from lower right to upper right (S.E. to N.W.), was followed by the eye in a downward direction (see Fig. 1). From the use of the words right, recht, derecho, destra, droit to imply good, correct, skillful, forward, and the words left, links, izquierdo, sinistra, gauche to imply clumsy, incorrect, adverse, retrograde, evil, it is clear that people do distinguish between right and left. No mathematician making a graph would put minus to the right of zero. However, the psychological importance of the sensation of rising or falling is far greater to the human intelligence than the direction from left to right. The associations that arise in connection with this effect are sometimes surprising. In the painting *Dawn Flight, 1959* (Figs. 2 and 3), the structure of the field shows a divergence from the left. Most observers, if their eyes are compelled to follow an upward movement, associate this movement with the motion of the sun (not shown), and recognize it as dawn. The same observers, shown the mirror image in which the eye follows the convergence downward to the lower right, recognize it as sunset. In images which can be viewed as flow, the downward direction will seem perfectly normal, but when these same images are viewed in the opposite direction this flow many well be understood by the observer as flying upstream, so to speak.

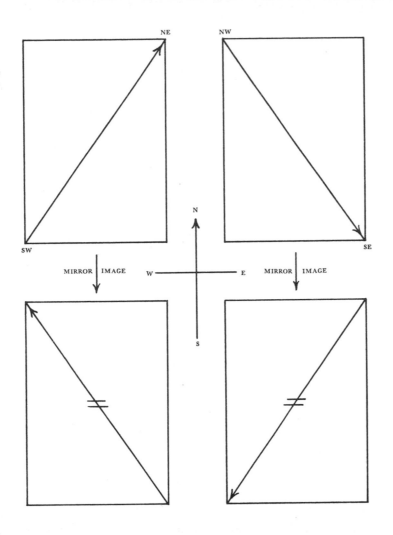

NE NW

SW SE

N

MIRROR IMAGE   W ——— E   MIRROR IMAGE

S

3

In the foregoing discussion of situation and direction, the notion of asymmetry has been implied. Like unbalance, asymmetry is defined by a negative, as if it were an exceptional modification of a normal state of symmetry. It is clear that this attitude involves an implicit assumption as to the structure of matter. The physical demonstration of a sort of inherent asymmetry, to which symmetry is an arbitrary exception, can be witnessed in the mirror image of certain objects. Seen in a mirror, the reflection of any tetrahedron, except for the regular sixty degree form, of a bedspring (helix), or even of a hand, can by no manipulation be made to coincide with its original form. This phenomenon, which has recently become of great scientific interest, was called chcirality (right- or left-handedness) by Kelvin. Without going into the rather obscure mathematical consequences of this position, it may be enough to indicate that the non-conformity consists of the "the wrong way"; that it is inevitably read in the wrong direction. This of course involves us with time and the essential asymmetry of its one-way flow. The consideration of this matter becomes clear in relation to our subject as it has to do with the mechanism of reversal of direction of motion.

The simplest case of the representation of motion, as in a graph, is a linear figuration of the locus of a point (i.e., the record of its displacement). This is a mathematician's convention and is not necessarily affective. But if two lines of different orders of curvature are presented so that the eye of the observer is compelled to follow them at different speeds, a comparison of velocities results. The conditions of presentation must be exceptional; that is to say, these elements must not be repeated in such a way that they may become part of a pattern or structure, the components of a web, mesh, or net, which are not perceived individually. Motion of this sort appears limited to the line itself.

When this motion is executed by splashing or projection, as for example in the work of Jackson Pollock (Figs. 4 and 5) or André Masson, the form of the drops progressing from circular, at slow speed, to elongated and linear, with increasing speed, amplifies the sense of increasing velocity along the trace. Where the projection is made upward with a rotary movement of the hand, it can be seen that the trace will have a parabolic form. The speed will increase along the direction of movement as it is registered on the canvas, although if we follow the parabolic path of any one drop, its speed is decreasing. If, as in the theory of "action" painting, it is intended that this gesture is to compel the eye of the observer to retrace the line as it was made by the artist, then the canvas must be shown in the position in which it was painted. Let us suppose that after its execution the canvas is turned upside down; the directions are reversed in view of the principles already cited, falling instead of rising. Also, that which was registered on the canvas as acceleration will be read as deceleration. The case is not, however, as simple as stated here.

A projection upward in a N. E. direction will be read as it is made. An upward projection in a N. W. direction can only be read as a downward movement of deceleration directed S.E. This matter has been brought very actively to our attention in the practice of print making, where the image shown is the mirror image of the plate or block. In general this reversal produces the same inversions as turning the canvas top to bottom, but as seen in reference to the non-conformity of certain mirror images the factor of time may still be incongruous.

Fig. 4. Jackson Pollock. *Number 32, 1950.* Duco on canvas. Collection Lee Krasner Pollock.

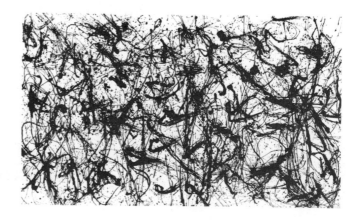

Fig. 5. Jackson Pollock. Drawing, 1950. Duco on paper. Collection Lee Krasner Pollock.

In these cases, although we have suggested a linear figuration producing an equivalent of motion, such motion is only observed against a field which itself may be either static or in motion compared to the line. The sensation of motion in a field or general structure, as for example in Lionel Feininger's *Yachts,* 1950 (Fig. 6), is in a way produced by a device dependent on persistence of vision used in the cinema, a series of repeated images, each slightly modified in succession like the frames on a band of film (a device used by the Futurists from 1912 on). The persistence of the image on the retina, as the eye is compelled to follow the series, enables those parts which are changing to appear to do so in an uninterrupted fashion. In the Feininger painting illustrated here the field is divided by parallel diagonals which give a series of parallelograms corresponding to rectangles in a static field, distorted in the direction of their movement. It is perhaps unnecessary to state that some time must elapse in scanning these shapes, and this produces a distortion like that of a slow-moving shutter in a camera photographing a fast-moving object.

The direction which the eye is compelled to follow, and in consequence our conclusion about which way the field is moving, is dependent on the same condition previously cited in the case of line. In observing the Feininger painting, the eye travels across it from left to right, and in order to keep the forms of the sails in focus one is forced to shift the eye back toward the left time after time. This produces the sensation of the yachts moving, although as we have seen, the operative factor is the whole structure of the field. Thus this device operates like a transferred epithet in poetry: the motion implied by the field is transferred to the object. The print *Unstable Woman,* 1947 (Fig. 7), shows a figure which, isolated from its background, has no inherent instability. Owing to the turning effect of the spiral structure of the background, however, the figure itself seems to be turning slowly in the reverse direction.

Up to this point we have studied the expression in graphic terms of a displacement or motion across a field, regarded as a surface, i.e. the apparent displacement due to color. It is possible to express another order of motion whose direction is inward or outward in relation to this surface. It is practically inconceivable that simple motion of this type should be continuous; the sensation of a spot of red emerging from a blue field is momentary and it arrives at a stable position in a very short time. The only exception leading to a continuously varying color space is that in which an ambiguity of position arises between two colors or color space and figured space, and the elements are alternately seen as being within or without.

This brings us to the last category of motion which will be studied here, a pulsation or rhythmic motion in and out. Rhythm can be defined as the repetition of similar elements at regular or recognizably related intervals. The repetition at equal intervals, repetition at regularly increasing or decreasing intervals, the condition of increasing intervals leading to a series of decreasing intervals, are all recognizable as what we understand as rhythm, so long as a connected and coherent system is present. For this order of rhythm to be seen in graphic terms as an in-and-out pulsation, there must exist in the elements themselves a certain state of labile equilibrium. Examples of this sort of equilibrium are familiar to us in the fluctuation of potential in alternating current, in the swing of a pendulum between two extremes of apparent rest, in the vibration of a

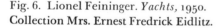
Fig. 6. Lionel Feininger. *Yachts,* 1950.
Collection Mrs. Ernest Fredrick Eidlitz.

Fig. 7. Stanley W. Hayter. *Unstable Woman,* print, 1947.

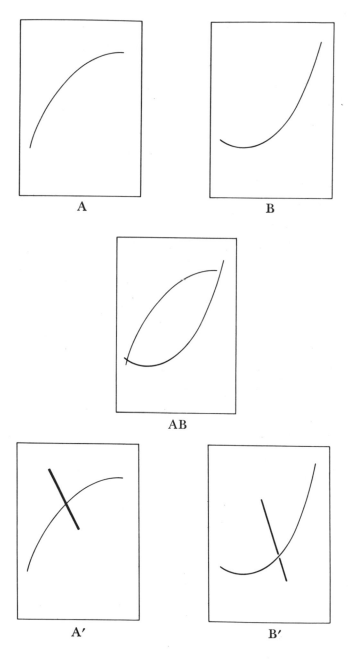

A

B

AB

A'

B'

Fig. 8. Diagram showing the perception of curves as concave or convex.

stretched cord. One case of this effect in graphic representation was brought to our notice in the behavior of curves in engraving. Certain types of curves cannot be seen as lying on the surface on which they are drawn or printed, but are immediately understood as being convex or concave to the observer. Notice in the diagram (Fig. 8, A and B) the curve A seen as convex and B as concave. Unlike those orientations referred to earlier, these configurations are not absolute. A simple device shown in the diagram (Fig. 8, A' and B') of placing a stronger line to intersect that which appeared to be convex will cause it to appear concave, and the interrupted line which appears to pass behind the curve which was seen as concave, has made it appear convex. In more complex systems of curves a third possibility has sometimes been found to arise: in certain circumstances a concrete ambiguity of position can appear (Fig. 8, AB). Here one sees a concave-convex position at one moment: a moment later it becomes convex-concave. In both cases this is perfectly clear and concrete to the observer. Such effects, which have long been known, are often referred to as optical illusions, as distinct from matters of fact. Needless to say, as we are dealing with that which is perceived by the eye, that "illusion" which is universally seen is all the fact that we need.

Another example of this sort of rhythm is the alternation in black and white of elements seen successively as objects or as background. Certain experiments in pattern of Victor Vasarely and others show these effects (Fig. 9). As we are here dealing only with means, no discussion of the expressive implications of these designs will be undertaken. Further examples of rhythm are to be found in the juxtaposition of elements of color of such form and proportion that the color space fluctuates and does not take up a stable position. In practice it has been found that cases of this sort arise from two very different operations. The most obvious one is in the use of two color elements which are complementary with relation to the spectrum of that light in which they are being observed (compare certain canvases of Mark Rothko). A much more unexpected case arises from the use of two very slight variants in color of one single hue with little or no variations in light absorption. Owing to the limitations of methods of color reproduction it is hardly possible to reproduce examples of these two categories, but the reader is invited to look for examples among contemporary paintings.

Fig. 9. Victor Vasarely. *Untitled composition*.

It is clear that the effects we have been discussing are of the type that mathematicians call series or progressions. Like the devices used by the Futurists they also have to do with the modification of a field rather than the action of an object or displacement of a point. As with the mathematical investigation of a "field" the use of these elements can be compared to the use of coordinates. Even on a plane surface we are obviously not limited to two coordinates, nor even to three. In an empirical system Buckminster Fuller has demonstrated four concrete dimensional coordinates (corresponding to the axes of a regular tetrahedron used as vectors). The use we have described of rhythmic systems could be seen as comparable to such a coordinate system distorted by uniform or uniformly changing velocity of translation. The understanding of a field of this kind does not of course limit it to a background against which elements expressing simple displacement, described earlier, can be exhibited. There is no reason to suppose that a work of art could not find its total expression within the modifications of such a field or in the simultaneous presentation of consequent field.

The expression of movement in these different categories, although quite distinct, may very well pass from one order into another. Lines indicating open motion across a field, its acceleration or deceleration, by repetition in series give rise to a field in displacement or pulsation. Motion in a closed orbit similar to that of a Calder mobile may appear to be open and erratic. Owing to the differing rates of motion dependent on the size of the elements, that moment at which the whole construction will return to its position of departure may be almost indefinitely delayed; yet in theory it must inevitably close the cycle at some moment. Thus if its motion were registered over a sufficiently long period it would be seen as rhythmic.

Finally, it must be realized that the existence of any one of the effects described does not necessarily nullify any or all of the others; they may all be present simultaneously. To make this position clear let us try to imagine circumstances in which all these effects may be there at once, even if they are not observed instantly but only one after another. If we study a small part of the surface of the sea (preferably in deep water with enough wind to produce "whitecaps"), we will find that the linear projection, at decreasing speeds along parabolic paths of the spray blown from the crest of the waves, is clearly of one type described in this paper. The apparent running pattern of several series of waves of different orientation, distance of fetch, interval and amplitude can be observed simultaneously and each element successively. These are clearly of the type of pulsation in a field in motion which we have discussed above. Then if some object such as seaweed, a bubble, etc. can be observed floating below the surface, it is seen to move in a closed elliptical orbit with the passing wave but not effectively displaced by it. Again a slow general movement of drift as current or tide may be affecting the whole situation. And inseparable from all these elements is the unidirectional flow of time.

Clearly the reproduction of the effects we have listed will not impart or constitute an emotional experience of the sort we vaguely classify as art. But with the means at our disposal to transpose a comparable orchestration of color, motion, impulse, and rhythm, one might well devote a lifetime to this project.

GEORGE RICKEY

THE MORPHOLOGY OF MOVEMENT
A STUDY OF KINETIC ART

An artist who uses movement may behave like a clown or a philosopher or a schoolteacher or a research scientist. He may use movement to attract attention, to intensify old ideas, to transmute the visible world or to construct new architectonic forms. He may use time like a spectrum of colors, space like an open ocean, the clock in everybody's brain to give a sense of scale, materials like an Escoffier or objects like a dump-picker. These artists, whether clown or classicist, have added a limitless dimension to traditional art. Limits reside, nevertheless, as always, in the seriousness, energy, inventiveness, and "talent" of the artist. If great talents use movement, great art will move.

The history of kinetic art occupies the last forty years. The *Realist Manifesto,* published in Moscow in 1920 by the brothers Gabo and Pevsner, terminates with five "fundamental principles of our work and our constructive technique". Principle number 5 reads: "We renounce the thousand-year-old delusion in art that held the static rhythms as the only elements of the plastic and pictorial arts. We affirm in these arts a new element, the kinetic rhythms, as the basic forms of our perception of real time."

At this time there had recently been three notable instances among artists of concern with movement. The first was Futurism. The word "Futurism" was first used for poets in 1908 by Marinetti in Italy. The *Futurist Manifesto* was published the next year, after which the painters attempted to employ illusions of movement as an intensifier and as an iconoclastic device. The second was the bicycle wheel which Marcel Duchamp mounted on a stool as a work of art in 1913 (the year after his Cubist-Futurist *Nude Descending a Staircase*) and entitled *Mobile,* and which he moved to his New York studio in 1917 (Fig. 1). Duchamp showed, however, by deferring his work with movement for years and confining it to optical phenomena, that his concern therein was Dadaist and superficial. The third instance was Tatlin's huge monument to the Third International for which he made a model in 1920 (Fig. 2). This monument was to be 500 feet high, of steel and glass, with a cylinder rotating once a year, a cone once a month, and a cube once a day.

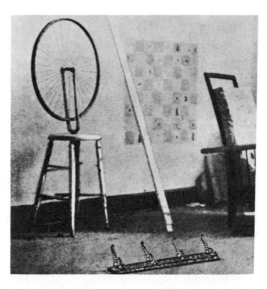

Fig. 1. Marcel Duchamp. *Mobile,* 1913.

Fig. 2. Vladimir Tatlin.
Model for a Monument to the
Third International, 1920.

The Futurist concern with movement had been recognized and evaluated by Gabo in the *Realist Manifesto:* "Futurism has not gone further than the effort to fix on the canvas a purely optical reflex . . . It is obvious now to every one of us that by the simple graphic registration of a row of momentarily arrested movements one cannot re-create movement itself."

The Futurists had in fact gone somewhat further with several constructions which moved, e.g. Giacomo Balla's "complessi plastici mobili", and Fortunato Depero's "complessi motorumoristi" referred to in the manifesto, *Futurist Reconstruction of the Universe,* which appeared in Rome in 1915. According to the Italian scholar, Carlo Belloli, these works by Depero constituted the "first known example of electro-mechanical integration of movement in a plastic work." Boccioni had written three years earlier in his *Technical Manifesto of Futurist Sculpture:* "We cannot forget that the tick-tock and the moving hands of a clock, the in-and-out of a piston in a cylinder, the opening and closing of two cogwheels with the continual appearance and disappearance of their square cogs, the fury of a flywheel or the turbine of a propeller, are all plastic and pictorial elements of which a Futurist work in sculpture must take account. The opening and closing of a valve creates a rhythm just as beautiful but infinitely newer than the blinking of an animal eyelid."

Gabo had a purer thought. He did not have any association with machinery in mind. He implied that it must be with "movement itself" that the artist be concerned. This was confirmed thirty-six years later, in an interview with Lassaw, a Constructivist sculptor, and Bolotowsky, the abstract painter, in which Gabo stated: "Constructive sculpture is not only three-dimensional, it is four-dimensional, insofar as we are trying to bring the element of time into it. By time I mean movement, rhythm: the actual movement as well as the illusory one which is perceived through the indication of the flow of lines and shapes in the sculpture or in the painting . . ." and "In my opinion, rhythm in a work of art is as important as space and structure and image. I hope the future will develop these ideas much further."

Gabo himself made only two sculptures which incorporated "movement itself". He had made a single drawing in 1915 for a complex articulated sculpture with arrows indicating the movement. He realized, however,

that in the current state of technology, the drives would be so cumbersome that they would eclipse the sculpture and "movement itself" could not be presented in a pure enough state. He thought then that the nearest approach was in the film and he was for a time intimately involved with the early abstract films of Eggeling and Hans Richter. His work entitled *Kinetic Construction* (Fig. 31) appeared in the All-Russian exhibition, which was dominated by the Constructivists, at the Galerie van Diemen in Berlin in 1922, shortly before the Communists rejected all non-realistic art and deprived the Constructivists of any chance to work, teach, or exhibit. The catalogue note on this piece read: "Time as a new element in plastic art." It was not till a decade later that Alexander Calder emerged from his toy-circus period and committed himself seriously to an art of movement beginning with motor driven, abstract, articulated forms (Fig. 3). Gabo meanwhile pursued the image in deep visible space, which also implies time by illusory rather than actual movement. His thinking influenced teachers at the newly founded Bauhaus, where Kandinsky, then in his most Constructivist phase, was on the staff, and where a colleague, Paul Klee, is recorded by Feininger to have had little moving constructions in his studio. Klee's *Pedagogical Sketchbook* shows deep interest in movement as a source of visual phenomena. Another Bauhaus teacher, Moholy-Nagy, built in 1930, two years before Calder's first mobile, a kinetic construction involving machine design, light, and complex movement (Fig. 4); this machine was made the subject and sole actor of a film, *Black, White and Gray.*

Between 1932 and World War II, Calder became the world-renowned creator of air-driven mobiles (Fig. 5). Others were working with movement, but in relative obscurity; it was not till after the war that creative talent began to explore extensively the further possibilities of kinetic art, concurrently with the revivals of abstract art, Constructivism, and Dada, which, severally and sometimes in combination, had come to dominate the international exhibitions.

Fig. 3. Alexander Calder.
Four Forms at the Fair, 1938–61.
Modern Museum, Stockholm.

Fig. 4. László Moholy-Nagy.
Light Machine, 1930.
(*Photo Ulrich Mack*)

These explorations have taken place in six general directions:

1. *Optical phenomena,* where apparent movement or actual movement of the object, or sometimes of the observer, produces some kind of intense sensation or startling revelation; for example, stretch a thread diagonally just above this black and white striped panel here below and move it slowly up and down over the lines.

Other devices are: the superimposing of a ribbed glass on other images, which, when rotated, provides vivid and unexpected metamorphoses (Fig. 6); a group of transparent glass plates, which, aligning themselves one behind the other as the observer moves, take on brilliant and changing colors because the plates are coated with a polarizing film; the dazzling and dizzying and apparent movement of brilliant juxtaposed complementary colors close in value; or the jumping before the eyes of black and white shapes interrupted to suggest overlays of contrasting designs or abrupt modifications of space (Figs. 7–9). Some of these effects are explained in *Scientific American,* May, 1963.

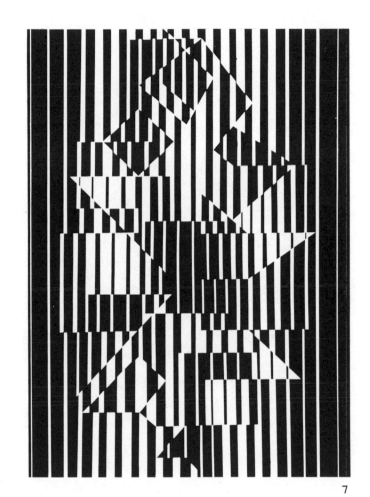

7

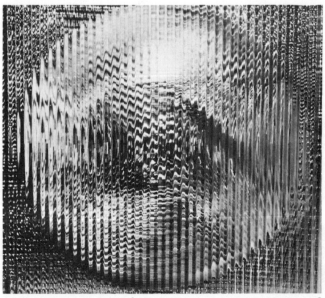

6

Fig. 6. Heinz Mack. *Light Rotor,* 1960 (in motion).
Fig. 7. Victor Vasarely. *Untitled Composition.*

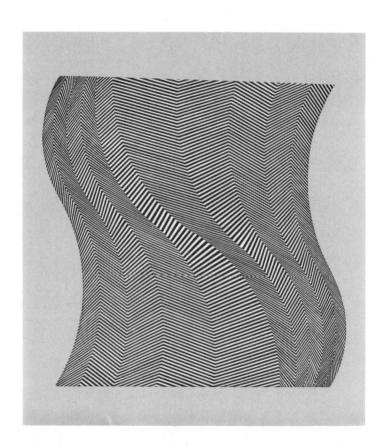

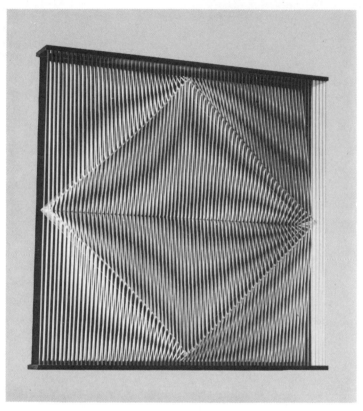

Fig. 8. Bridget Riley. *Twist*.

Fig. 9. Yvaral. *Instabilité*.

2. *Transformations,* where movement, often rapid, seems to dematerialize an object, e.g. the vanished spokes of a moving wheel; or where movement of the object or observer can bring about a profound change in its appearance, such as a painting by Agam, done on a single corrugated surface, which shows a succession of distinct compositions as one moves (Figs. 10a,b).

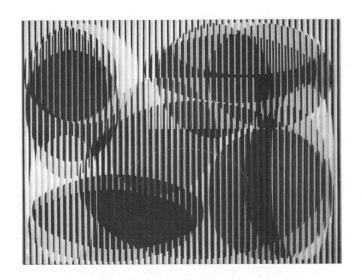

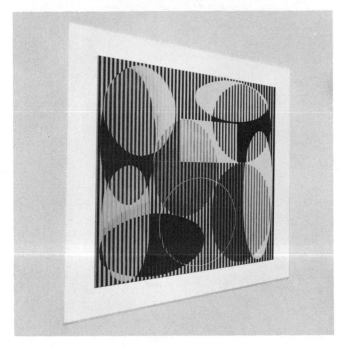

Figs. 10a,b. Yaacov Agam. Two views of a Polyphonic Painting.

3. *"Movable" works,* where the observer himself alters or rearranges the painting or sculpture, sometimes to the extent of a complete redesign of the space or the surface, such as a man-sized box by Kobashi in which ceramic balls hang on the ends of nylon cords riding over pulleys above (Fig. 11). The spectator, by raising or lowering the balls, is free to reorganize the space as he wishes. Similar reorganization is possible in the panels of half black, half white balls by Talman, or the rearrangeable structures of Munari and Mari, or the paintings of Gerstner (Figs. 12–15).

Fig. 11. Yasuhide Kobashi. *Plumbob IV,* 1960. Collection Patrick J. Kelleher, Princeton, N.J.

Fig. 12. Talman. *Kugelbild, K 100b.*

Figs. 13a,b. Bruno Munari. *Articulated Sculpture* (two views).

Figs. 14a,b. Enzo Mari. *Structure Number 495,* 1960 (two views).

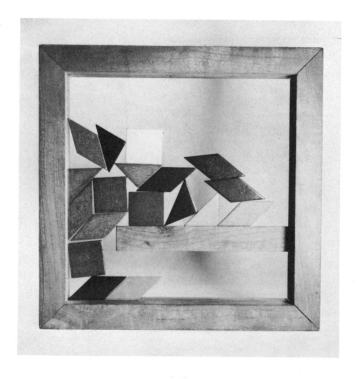

Fig. 15. Karl Gerstner. *The Tangential Excentric*, 1956/57.

4. *Machines* in diverse forms, driven usually by electric motors, with gears, cams, cranks, and levers pushing, pulling, lifting, turning. Some of these merely demonstrate, with insistent repetition, their own uselessness. Others dangle, wave, and jiggle *objets trouvés* of all kinds in a gay but deliberately futile exuberance. Just as Calder's mobiles have been perverted by followers to the mere dangling of objects in the wind, so the power of a motor has been used to make diverting in motion what is dull and meaningless while at rest. Once the cycle of motion repeats itself a more emphatic stasis sets in, for the motion itself is not designed. This type of kinetic assemblage (Figs. 16–17), is the most common, the most captivating for the public, and the least significant. However, there are resourceful artists who, while using a motor, defeat its tendency toward monotony and the obvious. Bury's twitching devices, motor driven through a simple combination of haphazard friction and slippage, never repeat, nor does Munari's column of spheres, while von Graevenitz's geared rotors are so numerous that the cycle of repetition would be longer than memory (Figs. 18–20).

Fig. 16. Per Olof Ultvedt. *Construction.*

Fig. 17. Jean Tinguely. *Fountain*.

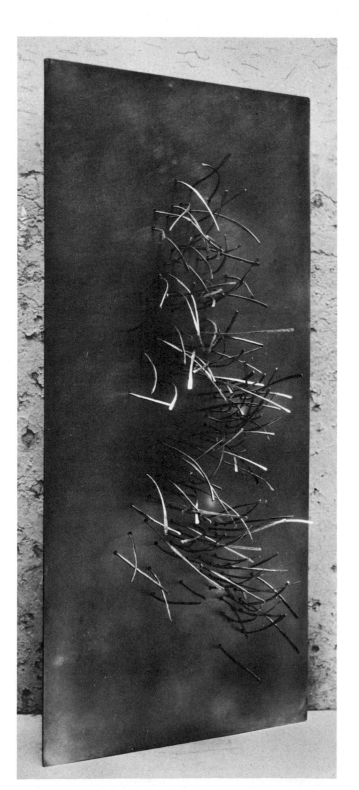

Fig. 18. Pol Bury. *Erectile, 1963. (Photo Shunk-Kender)*

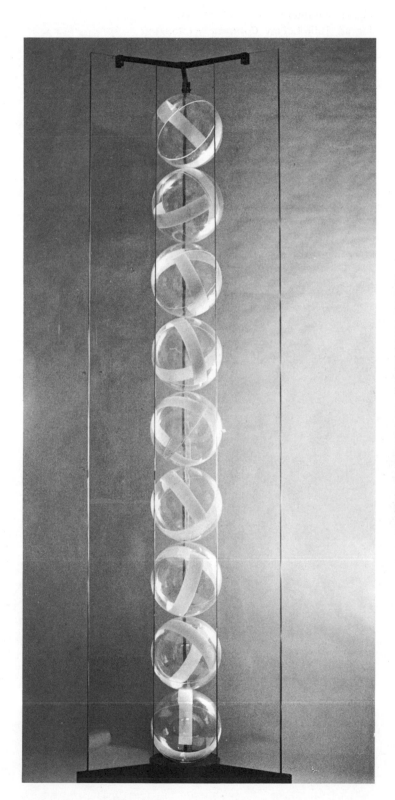

Fig. 19. Bruno Munari. *Nine Spheres in a Column.*

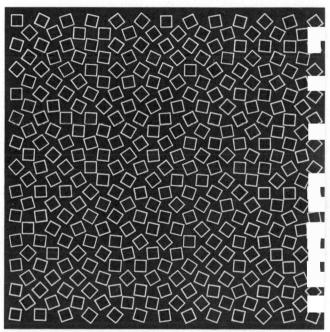

Fig. 20. Gerhard van Graevenitz. *Regularity-Irregularity V.*

5. *Light play dependent upon movement.* This can be the shadows and reflections from projected beams thrown on a complex of moving surfaces, or a series of focused images moving rhythmically on a screen, or spots of light escaping from a moving source and creating a sort of fortuitous firmament on darkened walls, objects and spectators in the room (Figs. 21–25). Though the idea goes back to Scriabin, the modern prototype of all of these is Thomas Wilfred's *Clavilux* of 1921 followed by such works as his *Aspiration Opus 145—Theme with 397 Variations* in the Museum of Modern Art, New York, which projects a kinetic light painting in color on a screen with a cycle of 42 hours, 14 minutes and 11 seconds, long enough to seem infinitely variable. Le Parc in his *Instabilité Continuelle Lumière* (Fig. 25) projects light from a moving source onto the polished interior of a metal cylinder and thence to a screen.

Fig. 21. Gunther Uecker. *Light Forest.*
Fig. 22. Julio LeParc. *Continuelle Lumière.*
Fig. 23. Gianni Colombo. *Great Pulsating Surface,* 1960.

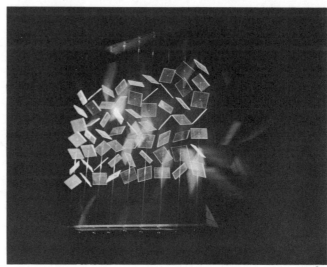

22

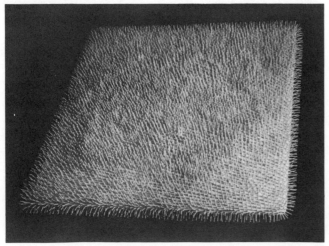

21

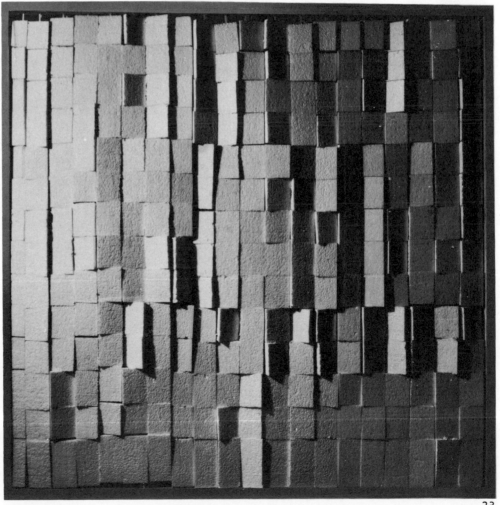

23

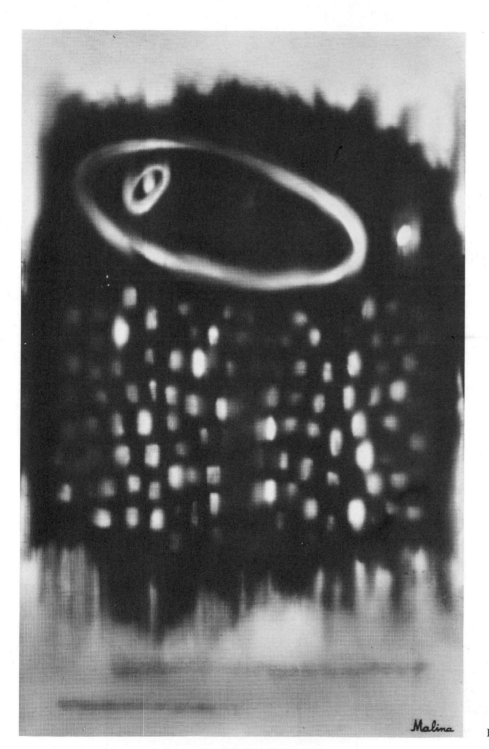

Fig. 24. Frank Malina. *Kinetic Painting: Polaris*, 1957

Fig. 25. Julio LeParc. *Instabilité Continuelle Lumière*

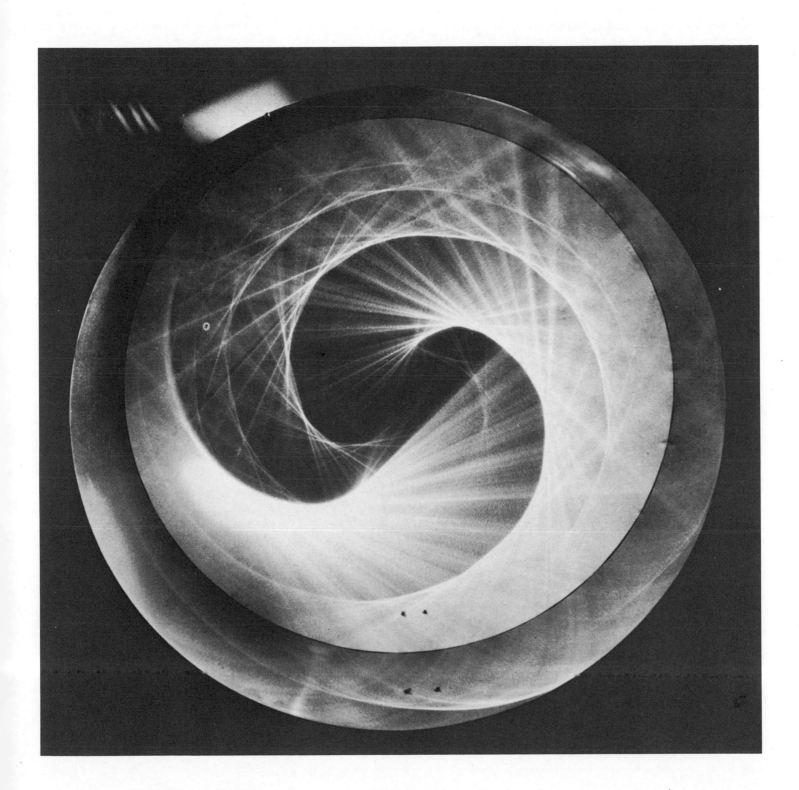

6. *Movement itself,* usually with economy of means and self-effacing mechanics. In this group are most of the serious attempts to find a form and to use movement to make a significant visual statement, "to make an art of the Museums", in Cézanne's prophetic phrase. Here for example would be found Calder's classic mobiles (Fig. 26), a slowly swaying combination of line and subtly shaped plane; de Rivera's perfectly tapered, flawlessly surfaced rotating loops (Fig. 27); the little-known Viennese, Georg Jung (1900–1957) whose seven kinetic pictures resulting from four rolls of painting on transparent bands moving to left and right, up and down, superimposed within a frame, make constantly evolving abstract compositions; Enguerrand's acrobatic jointed pendulums; Schoeffer's power-driven semaphores (Fig. 28); Takis' ten-foot-high swaying spring rods; Len Lye's rotating fountains and glistening steel rods (Fig. 29) and Bertoia's stand of bronze rods which give out a throaty song when brushed with the hand. Such artists design with "movement itself" as distinct from a movement which is incidental or accessory, like the trimming on a hat, or added, like the letter on a child's block, without changing the form. Their movement is as intrinsic as that of a gramophone record or an airplane in flight; without it the object would be something else.

Fig. 27. José de Rivera. *Construction, 80,* 1962. Collection Mr. and Mrs. Allan Guiberson.

Fig. 26. Alexander Calder. *Mobile.*

Fig. 28. Nicolas Schoeffer. Exhibition of his works.

Fig. 29. Len Lye. *Harmonic Curve.*

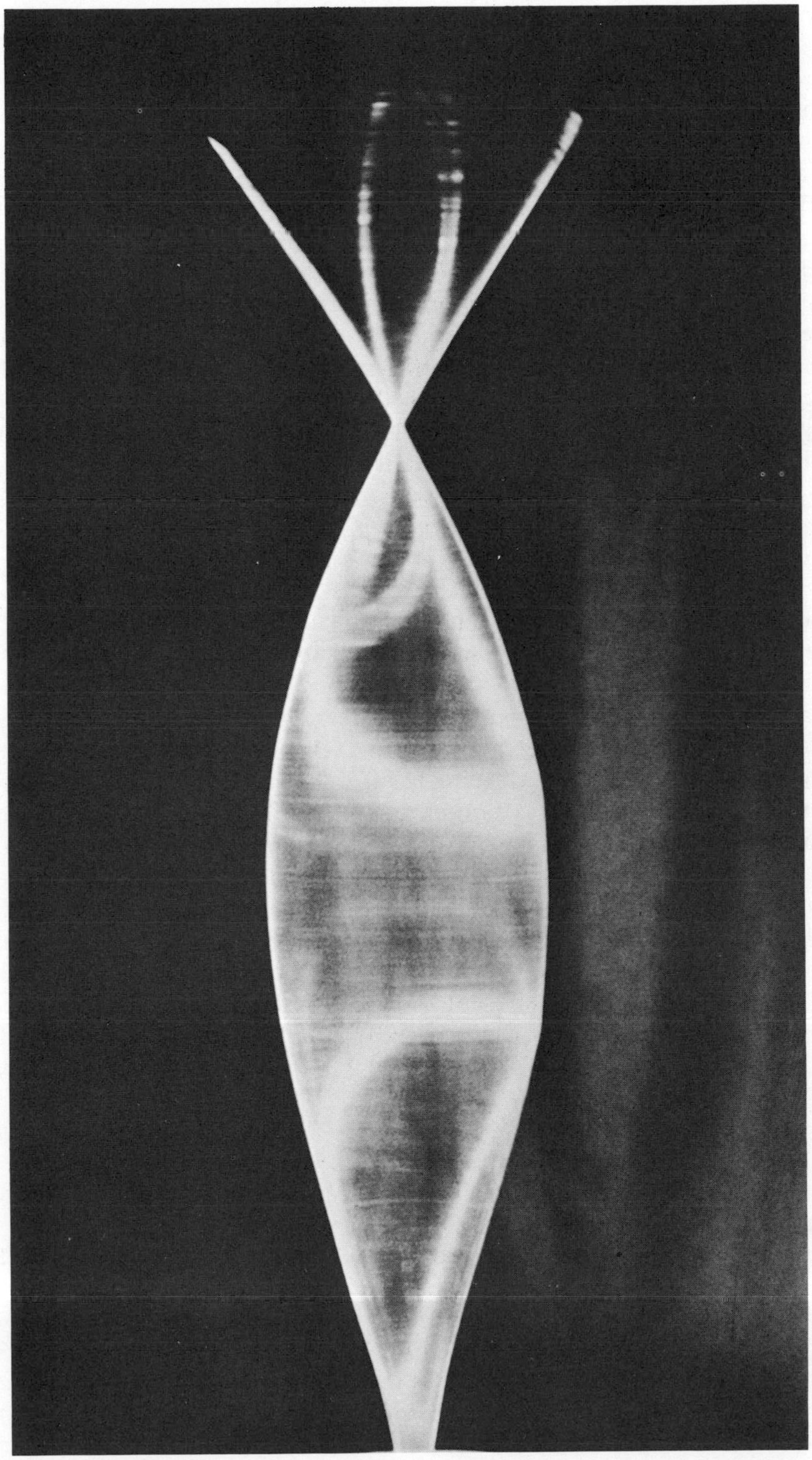

Like abstract art in general and Constructivism in particular, kinetic art has relinquished the human figure as a universally understood referent for "scale". In abstract art scale has, as a consequence, become meaningless except in the absolute sense of the size of the art object itself rather than the relative size of recognizable objects within the object. Since scale can no longer be inferred through comparison or association, the actual area of the canvas and the height and width of the sculpture become the scale. This can, paradoxically, make a large painting seem small compared to the monumental scale possible in a tiny Van Eyck panel or a Feininger watercolor. The inescapable smallness of absolute scale has led quite naturally to the use of enormous canvases which begin to seem large only when they are sufficiently bigger than the painter for his stature and reach to become the measure.

Within the abstract and generally scaleless idiom, however, four-dimensional art has an advantage. Motion is measured by time, of which we all have some rather precise perception. We can compute it, sometimes with uncanny precision; witness catching a ball, passing a car on the highway, or riding a surfboard. We can measure slow-fast, long-short, pause, interval, beats per second, period of swing, coming-toward-us, going-from-us, acceleration, vibrations-separated, vibration-as-a-tone. These are all measurable without comparison with other objects or recollections of past experience or relation to other events in time; they have a kind of immediate measure, which, in spite of the abstractness, can give a sense of scale. This measure and sense of scale have, then, in kinetic art, relevance equivalent to the human image and human scale in figurative art; even the uninitiated can bring their measure and find that the work contains something recognizable. Movement is not in itself esoteric; non-objective art which moves becomes accessible.

There is a danger here. The very accessibility may lead to the same kind of crass judgment that was exercised by the intelligentsia on the verisimilitude of Victorian art. They judged *only* what was accessible, the story and the realism of the rendering, and the *art* was as far away as ever. The Ghent Altarpiece was "primitive" while Frith's *Derby Day* became as popular as the royal family. Some of the popularity of Calder and Tinguely derives from this accessibility and it is hard to

know, now that both have become legends, to what extent their *art* is perceived.

In this measuring of time, the "interval" becomes all-important and it assumes many forms. It can be very short, even instantaneous, in the measurement of velocity or acceleration, or almost interminable in the measurement of a long journey into deep space or of the duration of awareness as compared with a momentary recognition. It can be interrupted, as in rhythmic sequences, and, if the intervals are short enough, can take on a new continuity as "pitch" or, in visual terms, the blur of rapidly oscillating objects. The drone of an airplane or the shadowy form of a hummingbird wing (individual impulses which appear continuous) are at one end of the gamut; stroboscopic photographs and oscilloscope curves (continuity shown as stationary images) are at the other. Many of Gabo's "constructions" and Pevsner's "developments" appear as static celebrations of kinetic events.

Any particular instance of movement takes place in its own time and becomes, for the artist, what a color or a shape is to the painter. The basic movements are surprisingly few and surprisingly simple. Western music has twelve tones. Kinetic art has scarcely more. Its gamut of movements must, of course, be within the range of human perception, just as the painter is limited to the visible spectrum, and they must be within the artist's capacity to control. Few though they be, they lend themselves, just as visible colors do, to an almost infinite range of variation, permutation, and combination. There are first of all the classic movements of the ship—pitch, roll, yaw, sheer, forward, backward, up and down, and sideways as in keeled sailing vessels, plus vibrations of all kinds. A bald summary of possible movements in kinetic art would be: linear movement along the three axes, rotations around them, and rotations around centers lying outside the object, nine in all. Vibrations are different in kind yet directionally they must be part of one of the nine basic movements. The rotations of wheels, the swing of pendulums, the reciprocation of pistons and the linear movements of cam-followers are special cases within this spectrum. Among vibrations, those where intervals are very short have led to extraordinary developments in sound, but to a more limited set of visual sensations. Intervals as long as 1/16 second in a low organ note seem to most people continuous; in the cinema, where the screen is dark for a large part of the 1/24 second separation of successive frames, persistence of the after-image prevents any sense of interruption. Even rather slow continuous movement of a line can look like a plane or a solid. A whirling propeller becomes a shallow disc. In his *Kinetic Construction* Gabo established the image of a virtual volume resulting from the vibration of a spring (Fig. 31).

At the still slower end of the spectrum of periodic movements are the pendulum, where the period's time is inverse to length, and the seesaw, where the period lengthens as the center of gravity is raised toward the fulcrum or as the relative proportion of the moment (weight x distance) above the fulcrum increases.

Tinguely, the Swiss neo-Dada sculptor of remechanized jetsam, in his pounding machines at rock-and-roll tempo, has employed a period which, while too slow to arrive at the continuity of vibration, is not slow enough to permit contemplation of the movement itself. This nagging frequency disturbs and also excites. Similarly the limbo between oscillations, slow enough to be followed and contemplated as separate courses through space and time, and fast enough to become a continuum, has perhaps a special character, its own kind of dissonance, and possibly a special intensity and capacity to incite. This is the tempo of fire bells, used by Tinguely as accompaniment to some of his works.

In music and the dance, and, for that matter, in poetry, the perception of order and the awareness of the whole depend on memory. These arts take place in elapsed time and can never be confronted whole. So with kinetic art. The movement unfolds, but what the form has just been or promptly will be are a matter of recollection and conjecture. If the order is so obvious that the form is predictable, it is a dull work. If it repeats in cycles it is a mechanical work and, after the first time through, not original art but replica.

The total vocabulary of motions is larger and richer than the short list of basic movements. For example there is in addition the whole gamut of accelerations and decelerations. There is, besides the "vocabulary", a sort of "syntax" of motion. One aspect of this is *sequence,* such as the merging of traffic lines at a tunnel entrance and their dispersal at the exit after a strict

Fig. 30. Drawing of a Geneva stop.

sequential episode, or the knocking down of a long line of dominoes. Sequence is a space-time phenomenon, an aspect of "movement itself" which appears in sewing machines, clocks, ignition distributors, automatic washing machines, and all computers. It appears in a visually striking way in the intermittent transmission called a Geneva stop (Fig. 30), which, if only it were useless, would be an important proto-kinetic art work. Sequence appears also in square dances, and in tennis. Since time is irreversible, sequence is also. The clock can again read noon today, but it can never read yesterday's noon. One can postulate plus or minus length, breadth and height; there is no negative time. So sequence must always involve subsequence. Being irreversible, sequence is, unlike the other three dimensions, impossible to arrange symmetrically. A "reversed" sequence is really a later sequence in opposite order.

If, while sequence is evolving irreversibly, the patterns placed in sequence begin to repeat their history, especially in cycles shorter than the memory, these patterns seem tedious and thin. However, phrases repeated as part of deviation and variation can be as useful in kinetic art as in music, especially as part of extended development. Exact cyclic repetition often appears in motor driven works; to avoid tedium cycles must outlast memory.

Another factor in kinetic art with which movement fortunately establishes a natural alliance is *chance*. Artists have always been alert to what chance would do to help them. Leonardo has a passage in his notebooks on the employment of chance stains on walls for landscape ideas. In a time when the "surface quality" of the canvas has become a zone of special interest, the factor of chance in paint-application has concerned such artists as Pollock and at times Dubuffet. Arp at one time used the chance falling of paper, glued where it lay, as a principle ingredient of collage. André Breton, looking for forms for Surrealist landscape, pressed two paint-coated sheets of paper together, face to face, and then pulled them apart to find in the blotted paint patterns the model he sought. In the dripping beads of metal on Lassaw's vertical and horizontal structures, gravity and chance work together. Lippold eliminates chance from the work itself, but permits it to operate through the great diversity of visual effects of parallax and reflection in his complexes of shining wires and plates.

Movement in nature appears partly as the expression of controlling laws and comprehensible cause and effect, partly as the product of chance. To combine in a mechanical device some similar factors of control and chance is a small step; witness the strictly confined roulette wheel and its bouncing ball.

Chance may be introduced either by the movement of the observer, which the artist prepares for but does not predetermine, or by incorporating in the object itself some factor of fortuitousness. Thus the disposition of Calder's lines and planes or de Rivera's curves at a given moment are determined only partly by the artist.

Motor driven devices do not lend themselves to the incorporation of chance, though they do not of necessity exclude it. The superficial and incidental flappings of a piece of rubber tubing in a Tinguely do not conceal the repetitiousness and lack of fortuitousness in his main design; in general his motor driven linkage comes around again to where it started and thereafter is tautological. Even if the cycle is very long, like Thomas Wilfred's color organ, *Clavilux,* sooner or later it repeats itself; the better one gets to know it the duller it becomes, just the opposite of the durability and renewal associated with great art. It is perhaps possible to invent motor driven sequences which never repeat, and hazard can be required to make its enriching contribution. In kinetic art so far, however, chance has been left mostly to the caprice of the wind or of the participating spectator. (We should perhaps note here that since a photograph records only one instant and one instance among variations and never the factor of chance, it provides a false record of kinetic sculpture, which can have no "correct" posture at rest.)

Motion reveals material: a calm lake could be a frozen one, while waves show liquidity; we shake a salt cellar; to find out what a fishing rod is made of, we wave it. With iron filings a young Milanese artist, Boriani, has made a kinetic painting where the particles are dragged out in strings, smeared, granulated, left behind, and dropped off by magnets moving behind the panel—a cycle of dust to dust. Calder's historic mercury fountain at the Spanish Pavilion of the Paris Exhibition of 1937, or the fountains at the Villa d'Este, or any other fountain for that matter, reveals through motion the nature of the liquid. Kosice stretches out the time dimension with slowly creeping fountains spilling the most viscous liquids. The tall waving rods of Takis show characteristics of spring steel and, in his later work, iron objects supported in a magnetic field in defiance of gravity declare to the astonished eye the invisible lines of force. The moving light images in the work of Wilfred, Schoeffer, Le Parc and Malina (Figs. 24, 25, 28) similarly materialize on a small screen an enormous space inhabited by a primeval and pulsating kind of life. The special qualities revealed by motion can become part of an artist's statement about nature, part of the truth he tells. Paradoxically he can do the same by *de*materializing through motion, like the vanished spokes of the moving wheel. The phantom spring of Gabo's *Kinetic Construction* and Duchamp's *Rotoreliefs,* which are no longer painted cards but orbs, have a place in history (Figs. 31–32). Len Lye's rods and clusters of steel lose all structure and become only light (Fig. 29).

Motion can equally reveal (or transform) structure, not only in the obvious way of showing cause and effect in a machine, such as the meshing of gears, the pushing of a crank, or the linkage of a typewriter key, but rather in the more intimate revelations of the link-to-link relationship of a flexing chain, the arching, resistance, recovery, and natural period of oscillation of a bouncing leaf spring, or the surface-to-surface zigzags of a light beam. Motion reveals weakness as well; in the case of Tinguely not only does the breakdown of the machines constitute self-sabotage by the sculptor, but when the

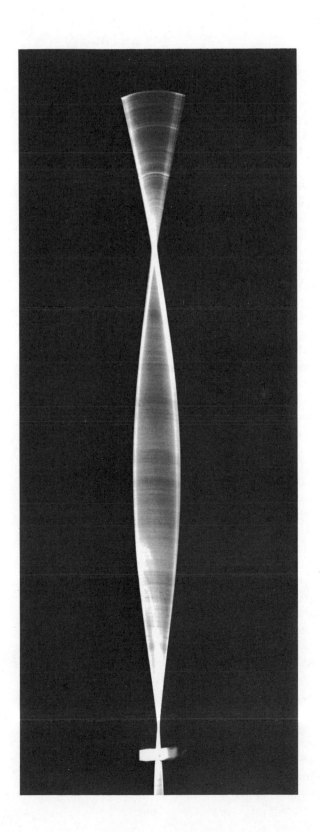

Fig. 31. Naum Gabo.
Kinetic Construction: Vibrating Spring, 1920.

Fig. 32. Marcel Duchamp. *Rotorelief*, 1935.

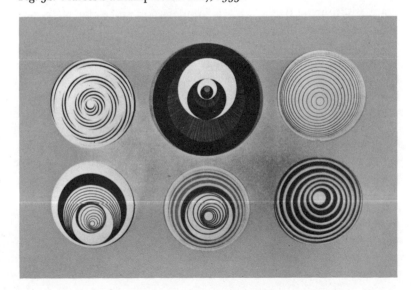

machines work, their motion shows that the assemblages of cast-off wheels, cranks, and junked appliances are too seriously ordered and constructed for him to be fully effective as mocker of machines, just as they are too ephemeral to be viewed as sculpture. The phase of Tinguely and of other artists preoccupied with movement in "happenings", assemblage, and *"nouveau réalisme"* is more properly viewed as *theater,* instant theater, one might say, whereupon the values they are concerned with become more reasonable. The temporariness of the episode and the flimsiness of the materials of the set are mutually suitable. It is the drama, not the object, which counts.

"Nature" is usually thought of by artists as the appearance to the eye of objects in the environment. It has been their great nourisher, whether recorded obediently by a Willem Kalf in the seventeenth century or modified beyond recognition by a prehistoric Luristan harness maker. This "nature" has been employed by countless generations as model, inspiration, and instructor. The artist has only sporadically transcribed it with verisimilitude. Nevertheless, in all epochs, even our own, "nature" reveals itself as the matrix in which the serious artist lives and moves and has his being. For the kinetic artist, too, nature is omnipresent and is always nudging his elbow. For him it is source book, example, competitor, analogy, tyrant, seducer, and also inexorable adversary. Nature has offered to the artist's eye landscape, figure, still-life and also geometry, light, intervening space (shallow or deep)—all well understood since the fifteenth century, and all fundamentally static. But nature is also "natural laws": gravity, Newton's laws of motion, the traffic laws of topology, the laws permitting the motion of a ship or the trembling of the earth, or the laws controlling the physiology and psychology of vision (Figs. 7–10b).

Nature is rarely still. All the environment is moving, at some pace or other, in some direction or other, under laws which are equally a manifestation of nature and a subject for art. The artist finds waiting for him, as subjects, not the trees, not the flowers, not the landscape, but the *waving* of branches and the *trembling* of stems, the piling up or scudding of clouds, the rising and setting and waxing and waning of heavenly bodies, the creeping of spilled water on the floor, the repertory of the sea—from ripple and wavelet to tide and torrent, the antics of people, schools of fish, companies of soldiers, heads of wheat, traffic jams, bees and ants—the "very many" in motion, the quivering of the aspen or the cowering of the panicked mouse, or, also part of "nature" in that it is part of his environment, the rotations and reciprocations in his car and his appliances, the swinging of cranes and bridges, the thrust, lift, and drop of planes, the random bouncing and rolling of a ball whether on grass, clay, or a roulette wheel, and those movements of sub-atomic particles never to be seen, but mapped and inferred from the tracks in the bubble-chamber and vague and awesome accounts in the press. The catalogue of the manifestations in nature that painting and sculpture have hitherto left out is endless.

Fortunately artists have not often tried to represent with verisimilitude the seething world around them in full movement, though there have been speculations about it and occasional attempts to do something. Since the Renaissance there have been thoughts of fashioning a mechanical man—there were stories of them long before Mary Shelley—and a few have actually been made, such as animated chessmen, walking dolls, and those men striking the hours with a sledge hammer on the clock in the Piazza di San Marco in Venice. Ironically it is when these attempts are more stylized that they are more successful. In the puppet theater, where diminutive and awkwardly jointed dolls together with a remote human voice create extraordinary illusion, enlargement of scale, and intense dramatic effect, the human image in movement is art. The Northwest Coast American Indians made moving masks of birds, animals, and men, often quite complicated and ingeniously wrought, with opening doors and dangling ornaments, but getting no closer to naturalism than to have an articulated jaw move up and down to imply talking or a face which opens up in two doors like a diptych, to show that there was another mask (and spirit) beneath. The very simplicity, awkwardness, and failure to achieve verisimilitude permitted them to become art. Thus it is not in imitation of appearance that kinetic art is served by "nature" but in recognition of its laws, awareness of analogies, and response to the vast repertory of movement in the environment. Kinetic art has remained close to the Constructivist principle that "we construct our work as the universe constructs its own", and that "efficacious existence is the highest beauty".

An artist who finds static painting and sculpture now too confining or overblown and yet does not find possibilities enough in the idiom of Calder or de Rivera to pick up where they seem (rather prematurely) to be leaving off, can still quickly reach a completely new frontier in kinetic art (as one can today in physics and mathematics) and work in virgin territory. The temptation to explore a new field in an age of discovery is almost irresistible. In certain epochs of change great honor is done the discoverers. It is exciting and challenging, yet it is precisely here that the greatest danger lies for avant garde art. No matter how great the fascination and drive to explore and roll back the frontiers of "the possible", the mature artist must deny himself this in favor of cultivating more richly a field he has already come to know. In art discovery is not enough. The kinetic artist especially must continue as alert discoverer of the possible, but he must forego the freedom and exhilaration of the perpetual frontiersman in order to make a cultivated, interpretive, and expressive art without the speciousness of novelty. Pioneering in a new idiom, with new material, even with a new aesthetic, does not make art, it makes pioneering. The artist must follow close on Lewis and Clark but he must live on a Sabine farm. Art is not made of what is new, but precisely, what is *old,* of what is, in fact, timeless. It is as hard as ever to put old wine into new bottles, and that is the bane of an avant garde.

A gifted person can readily paint an expressive, personal, perhaps primitive, and admittedly original picture with store bought paints and canvas and no technical knowledge at all. Even in sculpture he can, with only minimal technical knowledge, carve a piece of stone with pneumatic hammers, or model wax and have it cast in bronze, with a show of primitive force and freshness. But there is no primitive untutored clockmaker and no archaic and naïve kinetic artist. Kinetic art isn't anything (not even salvable junk) if it isn't assembled with considerable technical know-how. It must establish its four-dimensional existence and be viable in time. You can't push an object off a cliff and call this single event kinetic art, though it might have some significance as a "happening". Indeed there are more people trying to make kinetic art than are succeeding; this was clear at the 1961 international exhibition of kinetic art held in Amsterdam, Stockholm and Copenhagen.

With the exception of de Rivera and Bertoia there was not a piece there which would not have been more expressive of its purpose if executed by a good industrial mechanic or machinist. A lot of artists have had ideas that they are not adept enough to carry out. A personnel director's specifications for a kinetic artist might read like this:

1. Patient craftsman with knowledge of common machine and hand tools and a high degree of manual dexterity.
2. Theorist with understanding of balance, moments, friction, power transmission, gravitational forces, stability.
3. Conceptual thinker who can adapt a visual idea to a mechanical device and give it human relevance and "artistic truth".
4. Designer able to conceive directly in four dimensions.
5. Long range thinker who can keep an abstract idea alive during long hours, days, even months of tedious construction and adjustment.
6. Organizer with capacity to bring a complex structure to a single conclusion, without loose ends or confusing afterthoughts.
7. Sensitive, poetic observer of his environment and the human condition.

The kinetic field is far from crowded, even with half-qualified candidates, certainly in comparison with painting and even with sculpture. Probably the difficulties and limitations are not yet sufficiently recognized to invite the best talents to compete. Exploration is often unimaginative and pedantic, a mere extension of Bauhaus exercises. Performance is often slight compared to the possibilities, which frequently go unrecognized. Numerous technical possibilities in kinetic art remain untried. Most of those who have entered the field are still near the beginning of the epoch. Though experiments do not make art, a ripe art appears when the experiments have been gotten over with and a body of artist's lore made available, when talent can select its means from among the trials and errors of a previous generation, just as the discoveries of Masaccio, Uccello, Piero della Francesca, Castagno, Veneziano, and Pollaiuolo provided the basis for the form of the High Renaissance art of Leonardo, Raphael, and Michelangelo. Unexplored kinetic territory includes such possibilities as:

1. Water-driven sculpture tied as naturally to moving water as Calder's is to moving air.

2. Motion supplied by, with bodies supported in, magnetic fluxes.

3. Bodies supported by jets of water or of air, freeing the machine from the mechanical shackles that bearings become.

4. Movement of stretched membranes by pressure from behind as a form of kinetic drawing and painting (just opening up), or relief sculpture.

5. The movement of forms and the changes of color developing in the passage of polarized light through media of varying densities or subject to varying stresses (some work being done).

6. Non-visual kinetic sculptures—kinetic "feelies" which need not be seen; they could stir and alter their form, when felt, like Japanese *netsuki* or the steel balls of Wouk's Captain Queeg.

7. Greater use made of chance as a component, supplied, for example, by the movement of the spectator and transmitted by "capacitance" effect to the sculpture or painting. (The rather simple technical means for this exist, and have been used in commercial exhibits, but not yet for a really sensitive dialogue between a spectator and a work of art; the use of spectator sounds is being explored by an American, Frank Malina, in Paris.)

8. Kinetic work on a huge scale, as big as a ship for example, where time could be immensely stretched out.

Probably the field contains a future as undreamed of as Cubism or action painting were in Delacroix' time.

There will be few enough who will try in kinetic art. It is no bandwagon. The coincidence in one man of an idea, a desire to express it, and a command of the means, is as rare, as are talent, aesthetic sensibility, awareness of what the means could be made to do, the capacity to invent, the gift of endowing images with relevance, and, indefinable but important, the talent for success, which is probably another way of saying the gift of authority. These must all occur inside the same skin, or the same skull. Of course one cannot really write out the specifications for an artist; one recognizes him after he has made art, by his art. In the end the development of an art from primitive (and perhaps "popular") beginnings is made possible by, and also limited by, those who engage in it, or, more precisely, by the gifts and limitations of those who engage in it. These artists, working with responsive materials, within the visual idiom of the time, aided by the permissiveness of the group and the economic liberty the group provides, begin to create a *form*.

Constructivism attracted artists of extraordinary stature who have, by their authority, altered the appearance of our environment. There are no kinetic artists as yet who exert this authority to modify ways of seeing, as Gabo and Mondrian have done. There is, as yet, no master style-shaper in kinetic art, no canalizer of thought, no patriarch of *form*. Few of the artists at work in kinetic art have, themselves, much awareness of the form to which they are committed. Awareness of form in art is part of maturity; the lack of it is evidence of how young an epoch is. The form comes partly from the artist's idea and purpose, conditioned and channelled by the time and society he lives in, and partly from his energy, talent, skill, and technical mastery cooperating with and also pushing against the limits imposed by nature, human clumsiness, and the time-lag of his group. Only with some ripening of the idea and mastery of the means does a distinguishable form appear.

What would be the nature of this form in kinetic art? It would presumably be analogous to other characteristic ideas of form, for example the Northwest Coast Indians' stylizations, shapes, and treatment of human and animal features and method of carving wood, or the shapes and dimensions of Gothic space, or to the vocabulary of shapes, view of man, and treatment of the picture plane in Cubism. The idea of form and the permissible variations are consented to by some group with authority, like "form" in English manners, mocked as U and non-U, but real nonetheless. Its materials, vocabulary and idiom are consciously recognized by both the artists and the group. Though there are inventors, progenitors, and *chefs d'école,* form may be proposed by individuals (like mutations in the genes) but is established by fellow artists and other consumers. When Roger Fry wrote of "significant form" he was trying to find a universal equivalent of the distinguishable or identifiable forms of different epochs and cultures—of what Giotto, El Greco, Cézanne and Negro art had in common. His was an idea of form as a discernible factor in a value appraisal. The *form* referred to in these paragraphs is without immediate aesthetic or quality implications and is closer to *style* or to the *morphology* of modern art.

One might expect that the morphology of kinetic art would have been established by an artist as renowned as Calder, who long had the arena to himself. Using the catenary, the rod, and the free-form plane he made an image known throughout the world (Fig. 5). He put the word "mobile" into the language. Yet once he had hit on his image, thirty years ago, he developed it little. In fact the image he made was one of the most easily debased images of modern art, perhaps even more so than that created by Franz Kline. Calder has not clarified the *form* of kinetic art. It has been left to others to survey the scope of Calder's idiom and to establish his place as progenitor by their development from his postulates. The form of the mobile is too simple, too superficial—too easily imitated—to be considered more than a phase of a broader form. The idea of kinetic art is quite possibly as big an evolutionary step as Cubism, but the mobile goes no further, say, than Picasso's *Three Musicians* of 1921. Where is the Calder equivalent of Picasso's *Girl in a Mirror* (1931), or of Braque's later still-lifes, or for that matter, of Miro's more recent works, or of Paul Klee's view of the human comedy, all of which are within the morphology of Cubism. This is not to assess here Calder's stature as an artist or his historical role as innovator—but to note merely that he showed little recognition of the significance of what he himself was doing, or desire to make of it a deeper, nobler art. Thus

113

Calder's form is personal, rather than a form for the epoch, as Cubism was, as the stark woodcuts of the German Expressionists were, as the cubist-fantasy of Klee later became, and as, possibly, Tobey's magical surfaces and meaning may yet be.

It is only in the last fifteen years and quite outside Calder's work, that the indications of the form of kinetic art have begun to appear. Many of the kinetic artists, however, have remained in the "discovery" phase and are filled with wonder and excitement at the fascinating means and enormous potential of their art. They are occupied with exploration and demonstration of physical and psychological phenomena, not with creation and invention. Yet it is creation and invention, not discovery, which establish form and make the character of the epoch. So, when a museum of modern art wants to discern whether a new work "adds something" it is concerning itself with the very part which is not art; they should be testing for the presence of what is *not* new.

It takes more than the work of one man to establish form, though a great inventor may provide the base, as Picasso did for abstract art. While Picasso and Braque provided a base in Cubism the morphology of twentieth-century art was established by the schools their inventions inseminated. The base for kinetic art lies not in the work of its popular hero, Calder, but more probably in the Constructivism of Gabo, Pevsner, Lissitsky, Tatlin, and Rodchenko, extended by *de Stijl* in Holland and the Bauhaus in Germany and the U.S. After a decade of world-wide activity by several hundred artists the morphology is now beginning to be made. If kinetic art is to have a characteristic *form,* such form will be determined quite simply by two things: first by what range of visible (or tactual) moving constructions it is technically possible to devise; then by the way talented men adopt and adapt these constructions as a vehicle for their ideas. It takes more than a few diverting

experiments with new materials and a few newly observed phenomena to perfect such a vehicle. One could say that it took from the *Déjeuner sur l'Herbe* of 1863 to the *Maison du Pendu* of 1873 to prepare Cézanne's instrument, or from Picasso's *Demoiselles d'Avignon* of 1907 to Pollock's first exhibition in 1943 to establish the form of Abstract Expressionism. Though it is forty years since Gabo first designed a kinetic sculpture and thirty since the first mobiles were exhibited, it is only ten or so since any substantial number of artists committed themselves to working with movement and produced enough work to make an exhibition (1955, "Movement" exhibition at the Galerie Denise René, Paris)—roughly equal to the lapse of time from the *Salon des Refusés* to the first Impressionist exhibition. Most kinetic artists are working in isolation and produce slowly. Prototypes do not make an art form; only when a number of gifted artists will have had time to make many works (remember how prolific the early Cubists were) will kinetic art purge itself of its frivolous aspects—the coyness and toyness, the bemusing and amusing aspects of movement— and slowly, through its adoption by major talents, begin to make a monumental art.

This monumental art has not appeared yet. Currently (this paper was written in 1962) one sees novelty and wonder. One also sees how unwieldy the expressive means still are. The form is still too embryonic to show what it is, though it seems certain that it must not only embody movement itself, but also a component of chance, a machine aesthetic rather than Dada, and a high level of technical accomplishment. When the controls have been mastered and the waste effort pared down, when there is a school of second-generation gifted artists able to select from the efforts of the pioneers, then the *form* will emerge and, once recognized, will identify retroactively the patriarchs of what Hans Richter calls the Movement Movement.

George Rickey
Omaggio a Bernini, Variation II.
Collection Mr. and Mrs. McGinnis.

As we push deeper into the twentieth century, what recently resembled haphazard art symptoms are now taking shape to predict the future. One important new direction stems from diverse sources operating separately, yet together producing a strongly kinetic art based on tangible motion and tangible time. That present-day art is often motorized is not surprising in an industrialized world, yet mechanization is only one aspect of the new kinetic realism. Every radical movement of the last hundred years, regardless of how militantly abstract, claims to have extended the boundaries of realism. The Constructivists maintain they explored the reality of structure and materials; the Surrealists, the reality of the unconscious; the Cubists and Futurists, the reality of simultaneous experience; the Expressionists, the reality of inner feelings; the Impressionists, the reality of atmospheric light. Now another "new realism" appears, resulting not from suggestion, but from the use of *real time* and *real motion*.

Nor is this an invention of the last few years. Calder has long been preoccupied with the same idea. Only recently he said, "The mobile has actual movement in itself, while the stabile is back at the old painting idea of implied movement. You have to walk around a stabile or through it—a mobile dances in front of you." And very nearly a half century ago Gabo was already using motors to make both his paintings and constructions move. "My purpose," he explains, "was to introduce the element of *time* into our human experience, the point being that in visual experiences time is a constantly active element." Even the Abstract Expressionists are indirect forerunners with their ambiguous emphasis on the relation of time to scale—or why, indeed, have they insisted on such vast canvases? Their compositions, respecting no boundaries, no beginnings, no ends, are intended as continuous experiences. The exaggerated size of their paintings implies a time element, especially for the viewer. It is possible that the partial failure of this idea accelerated certain of the new kinetic experiments which today frankly depend on real time. When I say failure, I am only suggesting that regardless of size a canvas is ultimately circumscribed by its own rectangular dimensions, whereas a moving object demands attention during its entire span of activity.

Kinetic art lends itself more readily to public architecture than to installation in museums, galleries or private homes. Space and perspective are both prerequisites for the new mobility which discourages artistic preciosity. Artists preoccupied with real time and real movement tend to find single highly prized objects less interesting than galaxies of varied experiences. And yet these men are rarely anti-art. As a rule, they are concerned with aesthetic principles and technological inventions, not with negation or moral indignation.

Take, for example, Len Lye, who is experimenting with what he calls "tangible motion sculptures", an inexpensive medium staggering in its aesthetic possibilities (Figs. 1 and 2). With flexible metal strips and rods animated by synchronized motors, he combines form, movement, light, sound, color and time in an ever changing experience. Occasionally relying on only one supple shaft, he produces a kinetic image of extraordinary versatility, accompanied by music resulting from the metal's own vibrations. Variously colored spotlights playing on polished rods, the latter oscillating at controlled speeds, turns a single image into kaleidoscopic visual worlds where motion and light mold flexibility into a new kind of form. Though movement is real, form here is no less an illusion than in its painted versions.

Fig. 1. Len Lye. *Steel Fountain*, 1959 (two views).
Conceived as a model for scales up to 75 feet high.

Fig. 2. Len Lye. *Roundhead*, 1959.
Concentric circles of metal rings suspended on nylon.
Sculpture based on theories of a torsion pendulum.

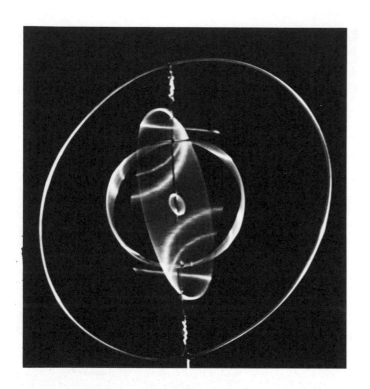

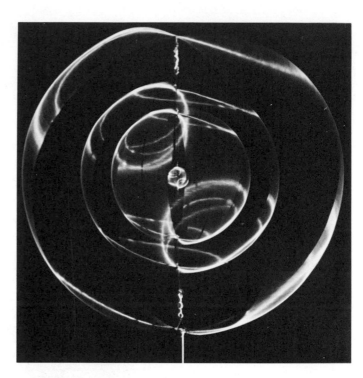

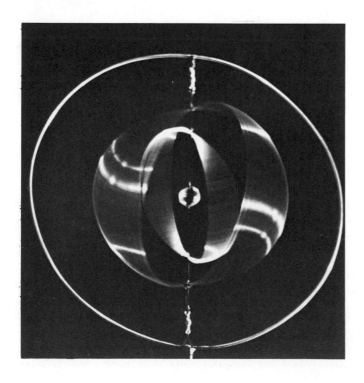

Not unexpectedly, Len Lye's interest in kinetic sculpture parallels his work with abstract films, for the cinema has long exerted a persuasive influence on art. More than fifty years ago the Futurists, also responding to the motion picture, foreshadowed our present emphasis on dynamics. In describing his sculpture Lye says, "Its shape becomes tangible in motion. . . . The aesthetic value of objects becomes secondary to that of their motion." For him it is the shape of motion that counts, not the shape of objects. Like many contemporary artists, he is more interested in process than completed fact, more interested in after-image than actual substance. Paradoxically his motion is tangible, but he pursues intangibles. He literally choreographs his motorized sculpture, depending on automatic programming that has been pre-timed and coordinated with impeccable precision to achieve innumerable vibrating, rotating configurations. Far from being anti-art, Lye emphasizes the "use of automation control techniques to extend the range of sculptured composition". In brief, he hopes "to arrive at suitable mechanical means for aesthetic motion composition". Nor does he join that group of twentieth-century predecessors who viewed mechanization with derision, satire and foreboding. For him, it is a tool as logical as the chisel was for the Renaissance. For him the machine is not to be scoffed at; he sees it as an optimistic, positive asset.

Very different is the work of Robert Watts (Figs. 3 and 4), who also depends on motors for his kinetic experiments. More closely identified with Dadaism and Surrealism, his constructions are part game, part ridicule, part deadly serious, and part deliberately accidental. With him, visual appearance is less important than psychological content. Constructions made of real objects (somewhat reminiscent of Joseph Cornell's "boxes")—dolls, familiar household gadgets, toys—move and intermove with frantic jerky gestures, never quite reaching their objectives, but coming so close that one thinks at times of Kafka.

About himself Watts says: "Within the broad scope of multi-dimensional media, certain facets interest me at the present moment. These have to do with an exploration of various time-space-movement situations through the use of both electro-mechanical devices and selected synthetic and natural materials. Within this spectrum, one may explore both 'environmental' and 'object' situations. . . .

"Now it would seem worthwhile to explore further. Various environments should be developed and studied toward learning about actual situations in such things as frequency and intensity modulation of light and sound, as well as movement in selected forms. It is possible for these environments to be activated by coded devices or by the movement of the audience through the space. In the latter case, the audience may be permitted to participate in either a planned or random manner. One can imagine an audience-environment where the audience becomes the sole activator and responds to itself.

"One may explore also a new set of 'objects', perhaps somewhat more related to painting and sculpture. Separate forms may be given the added dimensions of light, sound, and movement. These might exist alone or in groups within a given space. To various panels, more akin to painting, the same dimensions may be applied. An important problem to be studied here are the relationships of objects to environments. When does an object become an environment? What aspects of light, sound, movement cause an object to separate out or merge with an environment?

Fig. 3. Robert Watts. *Pony Express,* 1961.

Fig. 4. Robert Watts. *Victory,* 1961.

"Natural and synthetic materials must be examined in this new light. One can imagine that such things as water, earth, stone, plants, etc., could form a new vocabulary of media and take on new meaning. Synthetics offer the means for modulation and nuance, and permit new discoveries with transparency and translucency. New pigments and dyes promise to extend the color frontier.

"How it will be done depends upon the individual artist. Some works may be 'pure', some may consist of totally new materials, some of mixtures of old and new. In any case, the new forms should lead us to new experience and insight, hence to deeper meaning and broader knowledge of nature and man and his work. . . . Certainly there have been experiments with actual time-space-movement relations. Various innovators at the Bauhaus, later in the United States and elsewhere in Europe, opened the door to its broad principles. In this country, we know the work of Moholy-Nagy, the Calder mobiles, and the revolving sculpture of de Rivera."

Watts hopes eventually to design constructions for natural settings to be seen out-of-doors in relation to plants and trees, a scheme that could prove a welcome antidote to the static, pompous monuments we find in most public parks. "My recent work," he says, "has been concerned with engaging the spectator more actively by presenting him with things to do, so that there is a direct interplay. He becomes a new kind of observer, actually engaging in the activity of the work." Like Len Lye, Watts is interested in programming his work. He wants to "explore random sequences of events that may be cast into new forms, such as situations, environments and art games". The unpredictable he tries to make predictable, or at least he tries to incorporate it into a large over-all plan. In effect, it is precisely the unpredictable that he is exploring as a new art medium.

Along with numerous colleagues, he is frustrated by the limitations of orthodox painting and sculpture, those "standard, conventional forms artists have used" in the past. A strong believer in cross-breeding, he feels that "categories are breaking down and overlapping. It is no longer possible to call someone a painter, a dancer, a photographer, but only an artist." Most important in Watts' philosophy is his psychiatric interest in the observer. Though the Surrealists were psychoanalytically oriented, they were essentially concerned with themselves, not with the spectator. While probing their own hidden reactions, they rarely found the observer provocative enough to consider, let alone study. It is only recently that the situation has drastically changed, that artists are beginning to depend on the unplanned reactions of their audience as important stimuli.

In the last analysis, all valid art is involved with extending the boundaries of human experience. To this end the aptly named "happenings" happening in New York during recent years have been dedicated. Allan Kaprow (Figs. 5 and 6), a leading representative of this new art, explains how audience participation has infiltrated and stamped his work:

"My art has been moving steadily in a direction that appears now to involve some kind of synthesis of elements that belong to several arts. Words, sounds, human beings in motion, painted constructions, electric lights, movies and slides—and perhaps in the future, smells—all in continuous space *involving* the spectator or audience; these are the ingredients. Several or all of them may be used in combination at any one time, which permits me a great range of possibilities.

"Yet, though these elements all belong to separately developed arts, what I am doing is not a combination of these arts. This has been attempted with little success in the past and I believe the reason is simple in that (with the notable exception of songs and opera) they were conceived separately and were not intended to be combined. So, I proceeded from the everyday situation *rather* than from art, observing that in a room or on the street or in the country we have a natural combination of material coming to the senses which is harmonious because it isn't forced out of already highly developed and concentrated forms, i.e., art. Taking this as a clue, I worked with very simple elements and forms and conceived of them as events occurring rather loosely together. Beginning in this way, I found that a gradual refinement took place quite easily; and a 'total' art seems very possible at present.

"All this was arrived at, I think, logically, as an outgrowth of my long preoccupation with collage. Over the years, the pasted pieces of foreign matter grew looser, their edges were left sticking up from the canvas in an ever increasing degree, and I finally understood that I wanted to take them off the canvas completely in order that a *literal* space would exist between them, rather than the *suggested* space of traditional painting. (This space, incidentally, can be observed over the past 300 years as proceeding from the deep perspective of the Renaissance, becoming more and more shallow, until, with the discovery of collage in 1912, it was built outward from the canvas plane toward the observer with each succeeding piece of pasting.) Therefore, I hung large planes of canvas away from the original plane and then decided that this 'original' starting point could be done away with entirely. The whole exhibition room became the work; instead of projecting oneself into the space with one's mind, one could now literally walk among the parts.

"In the meantime, the environmental character of what I was doing became apparent to me and I began to include flashing electric lights, bells and buzzers, and these were distributed over the room. After that start, the sound was enriched by composing on magnetic tapes going to four or more loudspeakers placed around a given space, making it possible to have a sound begin 'here' and go 'there', etc.

"Then, among the visible elements, a whole new area of materials became available: cellophane, strings, plastic film, gauze, chicken wire, painted cloth or printed goods, aluminum foil, wooden or welded metal constructions, water dripping, mechanically moving parts, and, of course, slides or movies in several spaces at once. To this, one must add the visible human being who becomes part (automatically) of any given work once he moves into it no matter what he does.

"Now much of this begins to operate in time as well as in space and I have composed small, very abstract 'theater' pieces over the past year, which I have performed here and there. In these, the voice, the body in motion, the visible construction, the audience arranged in groups within the space of the piece, the artificially produced sounds, are all combined. There is no 'script' or 'story', no 'dance' score, no 'set', no 'music', no 'stage', no 'audience' really, since the latter has become only a passive participant in the work."

Though Kaprow emphasizes that it is not theater he produces, still these so-called "events" or "happenings" depend on time and movement in somewhat the same way that the theater does. Here danger of failure lies less in method than in content. For often the new practitioners turn to images recalling the trappings of Dadaism and Surrealism, occasionally borrowing so shamelessly that the results become little more than three-dimensional compositions of over-familiar themes, a kind of archaic modernism. For the moment, these young artists are important not because of any outstanding visual

Fig. 5. Allan Kaprow. *Environment,* courtyard of Martha Jackson Gallery, New York, 1961.

Fig. 6. Allan Kaprow. *Garage Environment,* 1960. (*Photo George Hurych*)

inventions, but because they have found fresh ways of involving us, of making us, the viewers, actively participate in their work (an end the Abstract Expressionists also advocated but only rarely achieved). We not only see a "happening"; we can walk through or on it, touch, feel, hear, and experience this event. We are confronted by it, but even more important, we are physically involved in it. What difference whether the work of art moves mechanically or whether we, on our own initiative, move through it? In each case, motion goes beyond suggestion. With real movement comes the added impetus of *real time*, forcing us to stay with the work of art at least long enough to insure the beginning of acquaintanceship. If the curse of split-second evaluation is thus obviated, another danger looms: that of confusing reality with art. Since art is not life, nor an imitation of life, but a re-creation of it, then the "real" can have meaning only when sublimated to this end.

One of the best known advocates of the new kinetic art, while often its most provocative, is not always its most profound representative. The Swiss sculptor, Jean Tinguely (Fig. 7), seeks to create environmental constructions but fails when his work becomes overly literal. Machines that devour themselves or are supposed to, machines that paint abstract pictures, that whang and bang insistently, are undeniably titillating but the irony of their symbolism is too often lost in literal transcription. At times Tinguely merely animates the Dada inventions of earlier artists, dissipating the original mystery and mockery in overstatement. Here is an instance when the poetry of suggestion is destroyed by translation into reality. And yet at best, his madly complicated, intemperate structures are cynical comments on the unbridled disorder of our present-day world.

Less well known are the kinetic explorations of Milton Cohen, a young man who is concentrating on the unlimited possibilities of light. This, of course, is not a new idea; one need only recall the experiments of Moholy-Nagy or of the now famous color organ. However, these earlier works were more closely related to the idea of easel painting, acting almost as substitutes for circumscribed abstract canvases. With Cohen, the idea of light is freer, encompassing a multiplicity of images so rich as to defy description. Projected by innumerable mirrors, these colored images race, slide, interlock and weave back and forth, in and out around the walls and ceilings of a room. A kaleidoscopic vision results, almost as if the dynamics of Futurism had been successfully freed from frame and rectangle; alas, only to face another limitation. For unless these light discoveries can be harnessed to more than single, self-conscious performances in given rooms at given times, they may become isolated productions, exactly what the machine was originally intended to avoid. Ideally, this fluid light technique would seem best adapted to public architecture. One can imagine it in the lobbies of large office buildings, the recreation rooms of factories and schools, the waiting rooms of hospitals.

In discussing his work, Cohen says, "As a graphic artist I have felt the need to establish a mode of expression which has its existence in real time, real space, real movement. To set imagery in a total environment, it has been necessary to develop an original method for organizing visual elements in a time-space progression as well as projection techniques capable of mobilizing imagery in space. In coordinating visual and auditory events, I have collaborated with composers who have conceived tape music consistent with this spatial idiom. The result may infer an emergent concept of art theater in which continuing and non-repetitive visaural events suffuse encompassing space."

Again there is emphasis on programming, a word that seems basic to much of kinetic art. For Cohen, as for many of his colleagues, to program is to synchronize fleeting images. His are not haphazard experiments. As Len Lye turns to choreography, so Cohen invents elaborate scores for his "light and sound manifestations". He admits that "the problem of organizing or programming the visual elements in time sequence is at once the most complex and most revealing aspect of this formulative space theater". Other statements by Cohen further reveal his aims: "To seek a definition of theater which pleases me; to exploit contemporary technological means to broaden mystery and subvert the machine; to put the image into time like music and the music into space like stars; to shrink distance between artist and spectator and spectacle; to suggest a museum of creative presence, of living performance, of spontaneous action."

Among these younger men a new world is opening up, a world far removed from familiar art "bohemias". Among the new group there is little talk of being misunderstood, but much talk of understanding the observer. The viewer is not castigated, but considered a necessary partner. Without his ears, eyes and powers of perception, most kinetic art cannot be vitalized. These younger artists need no closets for storing unsold works, nor do they rely on fashionable dealers or museum support. What they vitally need, however, are settings of adequate scale and scope where the public and the work of art can meet, mingle and interact sympathetically. The artist's new concern with the observer is in deliberate contrast to the individualism that flourished among painters during the last hundred years. If the preciousness of single works is now challenged, present-day inflated art values, and indeed the entire economy of art, may also be due for a change. Whether the artist shows his hand directly or merely deals with conceptual ideas, the results can be equally personal. But if the permanent, highly prized, unique object is replaced by ever changing kinetic experiences, the process of evaluating art is bound to be revolutionized.

Take, for example, the light experiments of motion-picture photographer Jim Davis. Though he calls them "paintings with light", these mercurial images are too volatile and impermanent to be compared with orthodox works on canvas. Evocative and elusive, they nervously come to rest on walls or ceilings only to metamorphose the next moment into totally new images. They cannot be framed or preserved, sold or exchanged, for they are in constant flux, the result of a complicated system of refracted and superimposed light.

Present-day kinetic art shows endless variations. There is scarcely a country in Europe or a corner of the United States where artists are not experimenting with real time and real motion. In Paris the young Greek, Takis (Fig. 8), is working with magnets. One questions this method, for the tendency to rely on gadgets can be restricting. Takis says, "I bought my first magnet and dreamed of using it in some way to bring about a perpetual movement by using the force of the magnet. I hoped to make some metallic object move forever. . . . What I wanted was to make what I felt to be really REAL. A magnet is not an idea—it is something so real that I was led to dream of making a Perpetual Motion machine with magnets." Why this young artist concentrates on perpetual motion is puzzling, for without rest, movement often loses meaning. Also perplexing is his preference for "an action in space" rather than an illusion in space. Merely to make an object move through space cannot be the final answer. Whether motion is suggested or tangible, it is only through larger meanings and relationships that reality turns into art. For deny it as one may, real magnets and real movement, if devoid of illusion, become fact and not art. Fortunately the magnetic sculptures of Takis jerk, sway, shake, twist and vibrate with a poetry all their own.

Occasionally multiplicity seems to take over. At such moments one wistfully remembers Calder's utter simplicity, his familiar forms put in motion by a wayward breeze, his precisely balanced mobiles recalling nature's own methods. With him, one does not question how the work is made, how movement is stimulated; one merely accepts them as one accepts blowing blossoms and falling snow.

The present development of a strongly kinetic art was inevitable. Speed in our time is a commonplace. Impermanence, change, revolution: these are our passwords. Every aspect of life reflects this tempo, even our toys. As the *New York Times* observed recently, "This year the die is cast for animated toys in general and scientific toys in particular . . . the toy industry is, in short, battery-happy, a trend which has been on the rise for some time but has exploded this year in a burst of hyperkinetics." What makes this comparison even more telling is the symbolic meaning that toys have for contemporary art. The more informal the new kinetic art, the more it relies on the participation of its viewers, precisely as toys depend on the children who play with them. The viewer ceases to be an observer and becomes a full participant. It is too early to predict how the new relationship of artist and audience will develop in the future, but from present symptoms it seems safe to expect a more permissive relationship—at least as far as the artist's attitude toward the public is concerned.

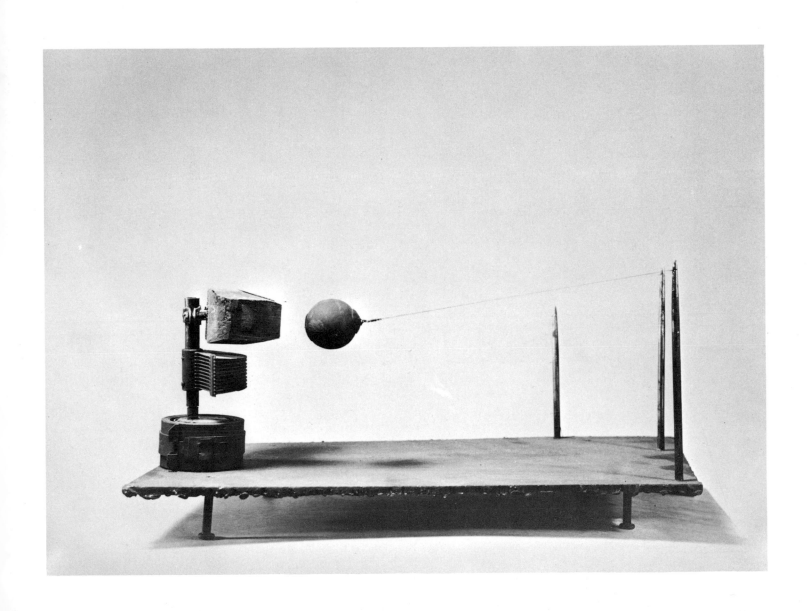

Fig. 8. Takis. *Tele-Magnetic Sculpture*, 1960. Iolas Gallery, New York.

a1:

Four sides of equal length, four right angles: a square
. . .

a2:

extended by the length of the side in the horizontal
plane: at both ends indefinitely . . .

a3:

given different degrees of lightness = a finite group of
elements; with terminal limits when either black or
white. The number of elements is determined by the
intervening grades: equal intervals from grade to grade
is the criterion. When there are large intervals, then few
elements; when the intervals are small, many elements;
here there are six between black and white, altogether
eight. The order is a natural one: each successive element is darker than the preceding one or vice versa. A
specific number of specific elements is arranged in one
series; all of which amounts to: *a structure.*
The movement: to disturb the natural order; to change
the location of the elements; to give their relationships
new import; to achieve different effects with the same
means; or to create with material (the principle of the
scale). For instance:

a4:

two elements interchanged: 4 goes to 5, 5 to 4. The sequence of the tonal values is interrupted; the change in
value is related to the change of position; the effect of
number 4 is a different one between 3 and 5 than between 5 and 6: the influence of proximity. Or: the action of optical, physiological, and psychological laws.

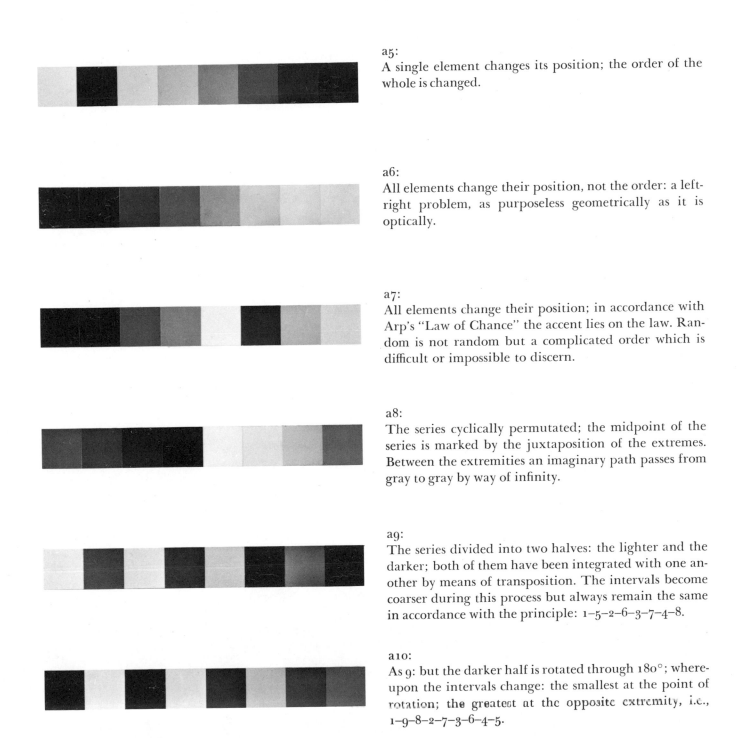

a5:
A single element changes its position; the order of the whole is changed.

a6:
All elements change their position, not the order: a left-right problem, as purposeless geometrically as it is optically.

a7:
All elements change their position; in accordance with Arp's "Law of Chance" the accent lies on the law. Random is not random but a complicated order which is difficult or impossible to discern.

a8:
The series cyclically permutated; the midpoint of the series is marked by the juxtaposition of the extremes. Between the extremities an imaginary path passes from gray to gray by way of infinity.

a9:
The series divided into two halves: the lighter and the darker; both of them have been integrated with one another by means of transposition. The intervals become coarser during this process but always remain the same in accordance with the principle: 1–5–2–6–3–7–4–8.

a10:
As 9: but the darker half is rotated through 180°; whereupon the intervals change: the smallest at the point of rotation; the greatest at the opposite extremity, i.e., 1–9–8–2–7–3–6–4–5.

b₁:
Instead of being in a series, the elements have been grouped together on a field: for geometric reasons the number has been enlarged to sixteen: i.e., the intervals are correspondingly smaller. The relationships multiply: to a one-dimensional left-to-right proximity, the two-dimensional top-bottom as well as the indirect one in the diagonal direction. Also: the spatial effect: background-foreground. Within the series a single element has two neighbors, at the extremities one; here eight, in the corner three, at the edge five.

b₂:
Grouped together on a field, the structure loses the natural order of the series. b₁ is grouped additively: here in the form of a hinge;

b₃:
in the manner of a spiral going inwards from without;

b₄:
in the natural sequence from black to white going from within to within;

b₅:
here the series is turned over along the angle.

b6:
The natural sequence: in the diagonal.

b7:
The progression in jumps: from one corner across the periphery into the center.

b8:
The principle of a9 in the arrangement of b2.

b9:
The elements are grouped together in the manner of the magic square; each column of four elements "added together" either vertically, horizontally, or diagonally has the same result, namely exact middle gray.

b10:
Sixteen different elements grouped together in a field, if moved this $= 20{,}922{,}400{,}000{,}000$ possibilities. The minimum-order is created by means of the structure: i.e. the movement is never without a law. Here: the order has been created by means of rolling dice.

C1:

Group out of groups: unity achieved by means of limited repetition; repetition by means of displacement; displacement as a symmetrical operation creates new groups; the groups of the same elements. Group b2 is displaced.

C2:

The second operation with symmetry: rotation, here around the lightest part, each by ninety degrees; whereby the groups remain the same, the length changes. The operation resolves itself: from unity to superimposed wholeness.

c3:
The third operation with symmetry: mirroring; here against a horizontal axis, the result on the vertical mirror axis. The part that is mirrored changes its orientation as well as its position. Mirroring: i.e., the operation with the highest degree of order; i.e., with the most symmetrical relationships.

c4:
For comparison: group b5 is mirrored. The characteristic quality of the original group has been intensified through repetition by mirroring.

c5:

No operation with symmetries on groups in the sense of c1–4: right from the beginning a structure which is conceived as a whole. The elements which have been repeated four times are arranged in a spiral in their natural sequence; they are led into the center from their four corners from light to dark.

c6:

A variation of c5: the inversion of light and dark. What was purposeless when effected in the series a6 here becomes a central inside-outside problem.

c7:

A variation of c6: instead of being in their natural sequence, the elements interpenetrate in the manner of a10; grouping is the same as in c6.

c8:

Second variation of c6: movement and countermovement; the beginning and the end are not displaced.

Double spiral: from two corners, i.e. beginning at two extremities, from dark to a dark center.

c10:
A variation of c9: double spiral, whereby one goes from light to light, the double in the opposite sense from dark to dark.

c11:

Spiral: led into the center from a corner, in the manner of b3, whereby the four series are in every instance linked inversely with one another. Inevitably in c9–11: the transverse proximity of the same elements. Discontinuity of the linear sequence: jumps from one line into the other.

c12:

The continuous movement from light to dark; but not in a spiral, not following one direction, but following two directions: from a linear to a two-dimensional surface effect.

c13:
Interpenetration; the elements in natural sequence interpenetrate in the manner of a checkerboard: from a gray center, rotating clockwise out to the black, the white and the black-white periphery.

c14:
The same formation as in c13 with the sequence inverted: the movement originates at black-white, not in the middle gray.

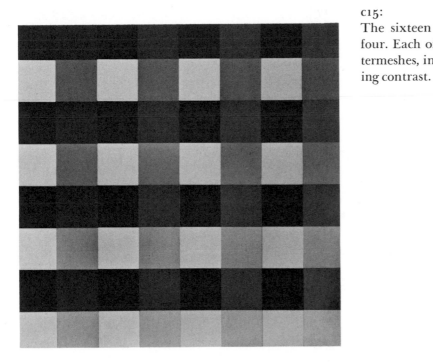

c15:
The sixteen elements apportioned in four groups of four. Each of these is rotated by ninety degrees and intermeshes, interpenetration and rotation, with alternating contrast.

c16:
The same principle as in c15: in addition, the single groups are cyclically permutated.

c17:
Grouping which confirms only halfway to a regulative principle; ordered but disconnected groups: b1–b8–b2–b6 are joined together according to the criterion "the white corner fields touch each other".

c18:
A mixture of a strict and loose application of a regulative principle: the light and dark half are mixed in the manner of a checkerboard. The individual position of each element is determined by chance.

c19:
Completely in accordance with the law of chance; mixed and grouped together while blindfolded.

Each structure is a specific order.

Each order is a special case among all the possible groupings; the more complex its principle, the more typical its configuration, and vice versa.

Or expressed differently: there are innumerable possibilities for groupings; there is a conceivable number of ordering principles; there are few complex regularities: there is only one "random" solution. The paradox is to be understood in the following way: the law of chance can vary by throwing dice, drawing lots, playing roulette, according to the telephone book, statistically, according to the whims of a monkey, with the help of a blind person—the result is always the same. We can perceive one thousand different kinds of order: but 100,000 kinds of disorder are perceived as one. And so as not to be misunderstood: I am speaking of structure and movement, of the movement of one and the same structure. I am speaking only of the abundance on the smallest field: how big is the world?

HANS RICHTER

MY EXPERIENCE WITH MOVEMENT
IN PAINTING AND IN FILM

THE ELEMENTS

Well before the first World War, I visited the Academy Julien in Paris and found the students there speaking with disgust about "le sal mouvement" in art. They were expressing not only their *opposition against* the paintings of the academicians in which hecatombs of naked women moved over enormous canvases or in which heroes or generals stuck swords into their enemies, but their *declaration for* the sacredness of the plane.

The students' concern at this period (and obviously that of the young generation as a whole) was to find the ultimate way to reconstruct the painters'·image of form and color and structure, to rebuild the canvas within its own static realm.

This mysterious message suddenly became implicit: form and color had become freed from guitars, madonnas, harlequins, nudes, and apples. I slowly opened my eyes as I saw how these objects had lost their old meanings.

At first I saw only a heap of fragments in orderly distribution on the canvas as if by the command of Cézanne. But looking nearer I found errors in this apparent order, holes into which one could spy, and inside one could see a new world in form and color. Then and there, I understood this message which promised a new freedom.

When, during the Dada period of 1918, I met the Swedish painter Viking Eggeling in Zürich, we understood each other immediately, for we found we were both concerned with how "to rebuild the canvas within its own static realm".

It is a queer paradox that it was this goal, pursued with an enthusiastic intensity, which brought us—to our own surprise—face to face with the problem of movement, or better, the problem of time. It has remained with me ever since, which seems to prove that sometimes historical tendencies realize themselves in individuals with or without their consent.

In these years, 1918–1919, we searched together for the elements upon which visual expression might be built. Eggeling "orchestrated" the line in an elaborated, quasi-scientific system of relationships, his "Generalbass der Malerei" which he had already formulated in 1917. I experimented with the positive and negative relationships of planes and surfaces on a more intuitive level. For both of us, music became the model. In musical counterpoint, we found a principle which fitted our philosophy: every action produces a corresponding reaction. Thus, in the contrapuntal fugue, we found the appropriate system, a dynamic and polar arrangement of opposing energies, and in this model we saw an image of life itself: one thing growing, another declining, in a creative marriage of contrast and analogy. Month after month, we studied and compared our analytical drawings made on hundreds of little sheets of paper (Figs. 3a, 3b), until eventually we came to look at them as living beings which grew, declined, changed, disappeared—and then were reborn. We finally could operate them like instruments (and that is exactly what we called them). A vertical line was made meaningful by the horizontal, a strong line grew stronger by a weak one, a single unit became important against many, a defined one was clear against an undefined one, and so forth. All of these discoveries became meaningful in the light of our belief that a precise polar interrelationship of opposites was the key to an order, and once we understood this order we knew we could control this new freedom.

Fig. 1. Hans Richter. *Dada Head,* 1917/18.

Fig. 2. Hans Richter. *Dada Head,* 1918.
Collection Mies van der Rohe, Chicago.

Fig. 3a. Hans Richter.
Exercise, 1918.

Fig. 3b. Viking Eggeling.
Study Sheet, 1917/18.

It was unavoidable that, sooner or later in our experiments, these drawings, which were spread about on the floor of our studio, would begin to relate systematically to each other. We seemed to have a new problem on our hands, that of *continuity,* and the more we looked, the more we realized that this new problem had to be dealt with . . . until, by the end of 1919, we decided to do something about it. On long scrolls of paper Eggeling developed a theme of elements into his *Horizontal-Vertical Mass,* and I developed another into *Preludium* (Figs. 4a, 4b). We had come to a cross-roads without suspecting it, because when these scrolls looked at us their continuity implied one thing unmistakably: movement! It was as much a sensation as a shock.

In the half-exalted, half-desperate mood of this discovery we decided to go on to "animate" this continuity; that is, to resolve the dynamic tensions into kinetic movements. But by habit we were so much motivated by our musical system of associations and terminology that we tried at first to "orchestrate" single elements painted on thin sheets of rubber by pulling these sheets this way and that way into a kind of "form-orchestration". This experiment was thoroughly unsatisfactory, and we then realized there was only one way to express dynamic energies as kinetic motion, and that way was with film. (It was only later that we rediscovered the scroll for what it was: an independent art form.)

But in the meantime, we had already started down another road to clarify our problem. In 1920, we published a small pamphlet called *Universelle Sprache* (universal language). This pamphlet elaborated our thesis that the abstract form offers the possibility of a language above and beyond all national language frontiers. The basis for such a language would lie in the identical form perception in all human beings and would offer the promise of a universal art as it had never existed before.

With careful analysis of the elements, one should be able to rebuild men's vision into a spiritual language in which the simplest as well as the most complicated, emotions as well as thoughts, objects as well as ideas, would find a form. To contribute to such a task seemed to us worth all the efforts and sacrifices we could think of.

From such considerations we came to encounter Chinese writing, which was based upon nature pictographs. These old Chinese characters were reduced to their most elementary form and were nearly abstract, altogether unlike the more or less naturalistic Egyptian hieroglyphics. It seemed that the Chinese had started 4,000 years ago—exactly where we, under quite different conditions, were just beginning—to use the archetypal patterns of form which are inherent in the human brain (a concept recently verified by the experiments of Prof. Max Knoll). On the basis of these patterns, the Chinese created infinite variations, and as freely as nature varies its pattern on a limited number of elementary forms.

For our purposes, we could learn three things:
1. That all characters were more or less an expression of the function or main activity of the object for which they stood. We experienced these writings as gesticulations.
2. There was a free but nevertheless very articulated aesthetic relationship of form from one character to the other which gave the sentence a rhythm. Very musical, to use our term!
3. There was, in the later centuries when the calligraphic tendencies developed, and in spite of an uncanny freedom with a single character, a very clearly defined composition of horizontal–vertical, round–straight, strong–weak, small–big, etc., etc.

Fig. 4a. Viking Eggeling. Three moments from the paper scroll, *Horizontal—Vertical Mass*, 1919. Modern Museum, Stockholm.

Fig. 4b. Hans Richter. Three moments from the paper scroll, *Preludium*, 1919. Katherine Dreier Collection, Yale University.

4a

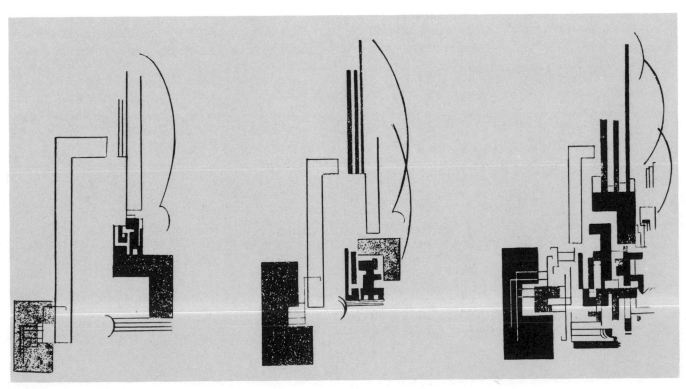

4b

As we were not studying Chinese to learn it, but to learn from it, we found there an encouraging confirmation of our way of thinking. We never forgot that what we "extracted" from Chinese writing did not make us anything of an expert, and did not uncover in any way the goal of Chinese writing. But as little as we understood, we found nothing more beautiful, nothing fuller of wisdom than this enigmatic forest of lines, this sea of movement. In the end, we had to acknowledge that, although we had learned much from the Chinese characters, it could not spare us from finding our own solution.

THE SCROLL

Though we had considered our scrolls, in the first rush of discovery, only as "material" to be realized in motion on film, we found that to be an error. For one reason: our first experiments in 1920 with putting our scrolls on film were devastatingly discouraging. The sensitive drawings which we had developed on our scrolls were the result of our studies of the elements of painting. They made perfect sense as paintings, but on film they were totally unconvincing. I stopped animating my scrolls, Eggeling stubbornly continued. The other reason: we found the scroll to express certain sensations which neither easel painting *nor* film could express.

This particular sensation, capable of being expressed only by scroll painting, lies in the stimulus which the remembering eye receives by carrying its attention from one detail to another, indefinitely, so that a phase-sequence relationship is built. In following the creative process, the onlooker experiences it in a singular way which the easel painting does not offer.

In this new experience of creativity, the eye is stimulated to an especially active participation through the necessity of memorizing. The creative sensation is accordingly of a different order, and it also conveys the kind of satisfaction which comes when one is suddenly forced to use a new or unfamiliar part of one's own imagination.

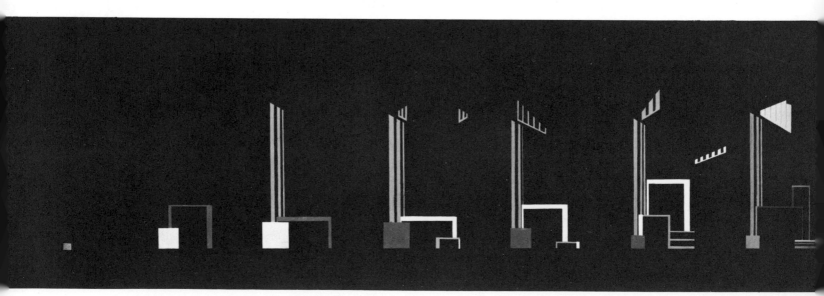

Fig. 5. Hans Richter. Scroll, *Fuge,* 1923. Museum des 20 Jahrhunderts, Vienna.

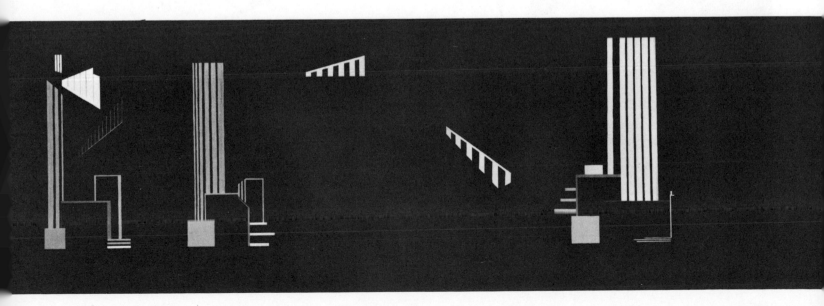

The scroll belongs to the realm of time, but in a special way. It is not physiological movement, but rather psychological movement. It is between painting and film. As a medium between painting and film, it is movement of the mind, movement which is kept in balance, but which still might break out any moment into kinetic action. It is therefore the ultimate harmony of non-movement, as a part of movement.

I consider the scroll as a new—and a 4,000 year-old—art form which will become fully recognized as a medium of expression despite the resistance of convention. It has to: there are sensations which cannot be expressed in any other way.

In the last forty years, I have developed two kinds of scrolls: one in which the eye of the onlooker connects isolated form-events (or "accords" as I called them); and the other kind, developed later, in which the form-events overlap and interpenetrate each other and flow on uninterruptedly (Figs. 5, 6, 7). There are, of course, many more possibilities open to the finder.

The present generation has not completely abandoned the rectangular easel painting, but the canvas itself has started to turn and twist like a caterpillar ready to change into a butterfly, or perhaps the other way around. The painting has swollen out into collages, thick and thicker, into gigantic, colossal proportions, into reliefs, the reliefs becoming half-sculpture and finally into three-dimensional sculpture altogether. Or else the painting has opened up backwards spatially, with holes ripped in the canvas, its surface furiously torn apart. The canvas does not rest anymore, it struggles to free itself from the plane as the dynamism accumulated by our age tries to explode violently into one form of movement or another.

Fig. 6. Hans Richter working on the scroll, *Invasion,* 1944/45.

Fig. 7. Hans Richter. Vertical and Horizontal Scrolls. Exhibition, Galerie Denise René, Paris.

FILM: ABSTRACT FORM AND FILM FORM

Few people have ever come to this medium so unexpectedly and with so much inner resistance. We knew no more about cameras and film than we had seen in shop windows.

In 1921, Eggeling finished the first version of his *Diagonal Symphony* after his second set of scrolls (although he remade this film three times before it was shown in 1922). I had completed my film *Rhythm 21* (Fig. 8a), so named for the year 1921. We were in a new medium altogether. The single image disappeared into a flow of images which made sense only when it successfully articulated a new element: Time.

Eggeling stuck to the graphic elegance of the forms developed in his scrolls, and he endowed the different "instruments" with certain well-defined types of motion. That is, he actually used these forms as if they were "instruments" of a musical composition. But as they were products of the painter, they put insurmountable obstacles in the way of the "filmer".

I dissented from the start, for I realized that the aesthetic basis of this new art form was the "orchestration" of time. It had taken a UFA technician more than a week to animate a single drawing of my scroll "Prelude" into a thirty second sequence on film. The technician was not very encouraging to begin with, and I felt like a blind man being led by another blind man. I wanted to understand better what I was doing and very much against Eggeling's arguments, I decided to start from scratch again, using the principle of counterpoint to guide me. This time I did not concentrate on the orchestration of form but the orchestration of "time", and time alone.

The simple square of the movie screen could easily be divided and "orchestrated" by using the rectangle of the "movie-canvas" as the field of pictorial vision. Divisions or parts of the screen could then be moved against each other. Thus, it became possible on this "movie-canvas" to relate (in contrast-analogy) the various movements to each other—in a formal as well as a temporal sense. In other words, I did again with the screen what I had done before with the canvas. And in doing so, I found a new sensation: rhythm—which is, I still think, the chief sensation of any kinetic expression.

A whole set of new problems now arose; they were a logical extension, if not a fulfillment, of easel painting but they could never be realized in the static medium. The tradition of modern art developed on a wide front, simultaneously with and embracing the film, as it explored such problems as: how to "create the rhythm of common objects in space and time, to present them in their plastic beauty" (Léger); the plastic expression of an object in motion under varying light conditions; the distortion and dissection of a movement or a form, and then its reconstruction in cinematic terms (just as the Cubists dissected and rebuilt the object in pictorial terms); the denaturalization of the form of an object to re-create it cinematographically with light—light with its transparency and airiness as a poetic, dramatic, constructive material; the use of the magical qualities of the film to create the original state of the dream; the complete liberation from the conventional, chronologically-told story by the use of Dadaist and Surrealist imagery, in which the object is taken out of its conventional context and put in new relationships, creating an entirely new content. The invisible could be made visible.

The abstract form in painting has, in a sense, a different tradition than the abstract form in film. In painting, it was the necessary and logical end of a development and the beginning of a new one. But

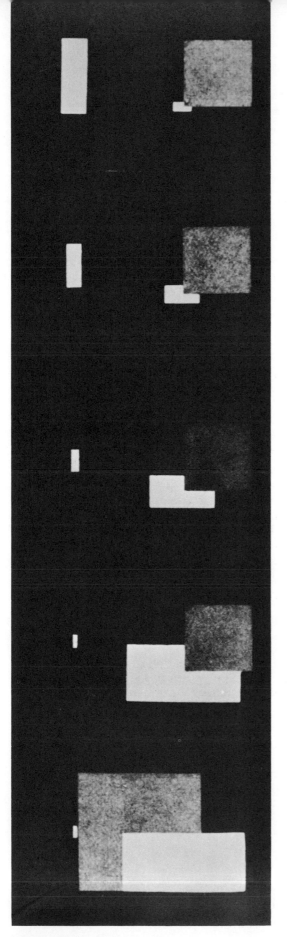

Fig. 8a. Hans Richter.
Strip from the film, *Rhythm 21*, 1921.

Fig. 8b. Viking Eggeling.
From the scroll, *Diagonal Symphony*, 1920.

abstract form itself plays a different role in film from that in painting, for film—by its very nature—can simultaneously utilize many types of formal imagery. And the reason for this is the basis of understanding film as an art form: it is not so much form-in-space as it is form-in-time. It is an error to consider abstract form as a type of imagery which necessarily and under every circumstance excludes all other means of visual expression in all the visual arts. For however true that might be for the plastic arts, it would be highly arbitrary to demand it as the final and definite solution for every *new* art form.

Film is a new form of expression, and aesthetically it is a new visual art (in spite of the more literary, and sometimes illiterate, use the film industry is making of this new medium). Therefore, the problem in film was, and still is, not so much whether or not to use pure form, but rather in which way can this new medium be approached, with maximum freedom, in order to develop its maximum expressive qualities.

All the refinements of line and surface which I had learned to control in painting, thanks to the years of analysis from 1918 to 1920, were not much use in dealing with the new problems. I tried to understand, first of all, the nature of film—its elements and its principles. Were they really identical with those of our art of scroll painting, so that I could and should transfer the theme from a painted medium directly onto film?

It is true that, through the experience and training of painting, I had come to develop the art form of the scroll, and so too I came to the idea of movement and film. But now I realized that the whole edifice of experience which we had built up in our scrolls made it only more difficult to understand film and to articulate this new art form which had no tradition whatsoever. That is not to say that abstract form was not also usable in film, but, in comparison with the more obvious problems (i.e., temporal continuity, interrelationships, and rhythms), it had lost the absolute priority it had in painting. And therefore, it became clear that our earlier work of analyzing the life of fundamental abstract forms was no longer the exclusive goal of our investigations. Film, as an art form, posed too many other questions, questions which were more important than the painters' preoccupation with form alone. But still, what about form?

Abstract film? Why not! *But* created under the conditions prescribed by the nature of film itself: the form and arrangement of fleeting moments (1/48 of a second each, or 2,880 pictures per minute!). In other words, the articulation of TIME!

I began my life work in film under these two conditions: on one side an age-old tradition of art with its set problems, rules and possibilities; on the other side, a new art without any tradition, and a set of problems, rules and possibilities still to be discovered. The way my work in film has evolved may appear to be inconsistent, but the key to its logic may be found between these two extreme conditions.

Chronologically and historically, it looks that way: at first, three abstract films, *Rhythms 21, 23,* and *25*. In *Film-Study* of 1926 (Fig. 9), an incorporation of natural elements in a poetic relationship with abstract forms. In *Ghosts before Breakfast* of 1927/28 (Fig. 10), mostly natural elements, articulated by strong rhythmical movement. Clocks, legs, ladders, hats, used as free forms, not respecting their conventional behavior or significance, but, nevertheless, assembled with a beginning (indicated by the clock at 11:50) and with an end (12 o'clock noon). These "10 minutes" are filled with totally irrational happenings . . . but they still make a kind of story.

152

Fig. 9. Two strips from the film, *Film-Study*, 1926.

Fig. 10. Strip from the film, *Ghosts Before Breakfast*, 1927/28.

STORY

It is here that the misunderstanding comes in; or is it a misunderstanding? We are not only accustomed by habit to look at films as stories. The flow of visual images *always* makes a story, whether there is a story or not; that is how our mind works. This psycho-physiological phenomenon is effective not only when common objects or human beings act out a regular story, but it works even when abstract forms follow abstract forms. At a screening in Paris of my first film, *Rhythm 21* (a study of abstract rectilinear forms in motion), a girl in the audience suddenly started to laugh hysterically. When she was later asked why, she replied, "Don't you see, it is like making love." So whatever else you do in film, you always tell a kind of story, with or without natural objects.

From then on I tried to discover more and more of these "secondary" possibilities of this new medium (secondary, that is, to *rhythm*, which I always considered the primary one). To achieve this, I proceeded exactly as I had proceeded before in painting. Eliminating elements of literature, I freely chose elements from the natural world as well as abstract forms in order to transform them into the primary expression of rhythm or "articulated time". As a matter of fact, I did not look at natural objects as literal elements. I did not even accept their conventional significance. I did not have to, since, in film (as we have seen with *Rhythm 21*), every object tells a "story", awakens some emotional or representational association, regardless of the context in which it is experienced. In addition to the emotional connotation of every object, I learned that there was an abstract, or purely visual, significance as well. And by making this distinction clear and by understanding its implications, I advanced to a new freedom of expression in the film medium. I experienced a new sensation of freedom, like the excitement of discovering my first scrolls and films back in 1920, as I recognized this new principle: objects could be used like abstract forms, and people like objects. In my book of 1929, *Filmgegner von heute—Filmfreunde von morgen,* I tried to make that point clear: "The value of an actor in film is not relatively greater than that of any other object" . . . and I illustrated this sentence with a beautiful circular roll of metal wire.

I was making films exactly that way. People, abstract forms, and natural objects were nothing for me but plastic forms, and these plastic forms, by stimulating my intuition, "dictated" the sequence, the flow, the rhythm of the imagery in all of my films.

After all that has been said (and I hope it is clear so far), we still have to go one step further. As film, by its very nature, always evokes some kind of a story, could this story not also be planned—not, however, as an extension of literature (as in the normal film), but in the poetic realm—and without deviating from the visual concepts of film. In other words, is there still another secondary dimension which may be added?

To allow chance to play its role, to watch stories develop which I had not planned, to walk the tightrope of associations and to watch with an open mind how the unexpected, and often unknown content is born, that is where my experience as Dadaist (or Surrealist) and those as an abstract painter overlap. (In the case to be treated here, the difference between Dadaism and Surrealism is not essential.)

One evening, for instance, I went to the singer Libby Holman's house in Stamford for dinner. Arriving there, I saw a big empty swimming pool, painted very green, and beside it about a dozen elegant suitcases . . . melting together into one image in the dusk of the evening. This strange image intrigued and preoccupied me so much that I could hardly eat. The incongruency disturbed and attracted me. This swimming pool and these suitcases became then the main actors of the last episode of my film *8 x 8* (Fig. 11), a surreal event as an expression of surreal experience. This experience had at first no name, but crystallized somnambulistically, so to speak, first into a vague continuity (with the analytical help of my wife), and finally into a story. So what had started out not at all as a story grew by the marriage of the visual material with the conscious mind (which tried to understand the implications) into a surreal story.

I may use abstract forms poetically, as human beings—and can use human beings as abstractly as a rectangle—but whatever element I use, in whatever way, a story will develop. The medium of film turns everything into a story, because IT MOVES.

And when I edit a film, the process is not so very different from painting. The story in film is born by the rhythm of form and color (plus sound). I compose moving forms and the story develops always by, with and through an *object;* it may be a red coat, a black ball, a blue cable, a fluttering paper, a suitcase or an abstract form. In painting the work develops from the vision of some tension incorporated in a line, surface, even a spot. Painting and film are both forms of visual expression. In many ways their problems overlap, in others they differ.

156

Fig. 11. Libby Holman's swimming pool used for a scene in the film *8 x 8*, 1957.

Fig. 12. Still from the film, *Dreams that Money Can Buy*, 1947.

ROBERT GESSNER

SEVEN FACES OF TIME:
AN AESTHETIC FOR CINEMA

No art is more involved with motion than cinema, and yet this chief characteristic, which endows it with its luminous uniqueness, is little noted, nor much appreciated. Professional critics confine reflections to performances, narrative meanings, sociology, or—that nebulous category—direction; visual illiterates see only actors, plot, and setting. While cinema is often recognized as the most persuasive of the arts, the *raison d'être* for its power is largely, and curiously, ignored.

This is not to insist that art needs theory in order to be appreciated, but a more profound understanding, at least, of an art's particular possibilities may enhance aesthetic judgment as well as quicken sensory experience. The personal prospect involved should make the adventure worthwhile. Nonetheless, cinema, alone among the major arts, is practiced apart from any aesthetical authority, rooted and flowering in an accumulated appreciation of its *sui generis* characteristics. Actually, this phenomenon appears to be the exception in the history of major art forms.

The reasons are not difficult to recognize. In the main, craftsmen and artists who have sought personal rewards, psychological or pecuniary, in cinema over the last two generations, were trained, if at all, in vaudeville, circus, theatrical and literary concepts; even those raised on backlots in a movie atmosphere did so in a milieu conditioned by the traditions of other entertainments. An industry matured before an art was born. Thus, commercial considerations, having so long dominated the creative and exhibitive processes, made a rare film of artistic merit appear to be an isolated exception. Such milestones from the time of *The Life of an American Fireman* (1903) and *The Birth of a Nation* (1915) through to *Citizen Kane* (1941), *8½* (1963), and *Tom Jones* (1963)—to name only a few—have been viewed mainly as mileage markers, rather than as topographical evidence illuminating the nature of the road. A parallel misreading of an art form would be an exaltation of man's progress from hieroglyphics to the fast rotary press without considering the aesthetics of literature. The language of motion, however, has been so successful as entertainment and as a persuader for advertisers, with instant satisfaction, that few creators or academicians were inclined—or are today so inclined—to interpret movies and TV with serious analytical respect as an art form. Motion, unfortunately, like the process of

breathing, has been taken for granted. "I've grown accustomed to her face," sang Professor Higgins, "like breathing out and breathing in."

The Russian directors, L. V. Kuleshov, V. I. Pudovkin, and S. M. Eisenstein, were the first in the late 'twenties to write on "filmic time" and "dynamization in space",[1] having graciously credited the "Americans"—mainly D. W. Griffith—as "the first to discover in the filmplay the presence of peculiar possibilities of its own".[2] The Bauhaus group in the same period were employing the terms "space-motion" and "space-time".[3] It remained for Erwin Panofsky in a lecture in 1934 (later published in *Critique*) to equate the terms: "These unique and specific possibilities can be defined as *dynamization of space* and, accordingly, *spatialization of time*."[4]

Professor Panofsky, more than any scholar of the preceding generation, opened our eyes to cinema as an independent art, divorced from the theater and not its child, step-sister, or handmaiden. A few others, scholars and artists, welcomed cinema as a major art, freed by camera and editing from the tyranny of dialogue. It was clear that mere recording of theatrical forms onto celluloid was adequate for box office, but stultifying to cinematic creativity.

We see now, however, that a description of cinema as a time-space form, while refreshing, is inadequate; the term, being all-inclusive, means everything and nothing. What evokes a "dynamization of space" or a "spatialization of time"? What makes cinema a kinetic art form? The confusions in craft execution as well as the chaos in criticism indicate that cinema suffers from the absence of patterns and structures, generically authentic, that could refocus its possibilities. Other arts may suffer from this problem, but in cinema it is no longer a growing pain; rather, the lack of fundamental insights is a headache that has prolonged puberty. Even as the most "potent social form of visual communication"[5]—an excellent condensation of its values—cinema lacks in aesthetic judgment what it enjoys abundantly in aesthetic experience.

Nearly three and a half decades ago, D. W. Prall described aesthetic judgment: "It is not of course aesthetic experience as such, about which psychology and psychological aesthetics have had so much to say. Nor is it criticism, which is occupied largely with assessing and analyzing relative aesthetic values in a scale of value or placing a given example under some familiar rubric, as when we notice that a play is a farce or a college building pseudo-Gothic. Aesthetic judgment is distinguished from aesthetic experience as such by the simple fact that it follows and records such experience after the experience has been had and with reference to what was experienced."[6]

The ability to record direct aesthetic experience in terms of feeling and meaning would depend largely on an awareness of the internal means that determine form as well as a recognition of the inseparability of means and content. Cinema, of all the arts, has the most multiple means of movement: motion is its life-blood.

As life is movement of some sort, the moment in cinema that comes alive for us is an artistic experience and should lead to an aesthetic judgment, based on an artistic discipline. Just as the difference between recording and creating is the difference between craft and art, so cinematic experience achieves immortality when it creates movement that is both sensory and intellectual. William Faulkner observed: "The aim of every artist is to arrest motion, which is life, by artificial means and hold it fixed so that a hundred years later, when a stranger looks at it, it moves again since it is life."[7]

How much more poignant is Faulkner's observation when all the variable structures and patterns in cinema are utilized. Thus far, it seems evident, the plastic potentiality—the evocation of feeling and meaning through visual stimuli—has been handicapped by an overemphasis on objects in space, that is, on actors and locale, on inanimate subjects and sound. The theater-orientated director and the popular-minded screen playwright seek to stimulate the eye through manipulation of persons and things, or—stated theoretically—primarily through a *dynamization of space*. Thus a spectacle like *Ben Hur* (1959), except for the chariot races, may bore the visually illiterate with its "acting and talk", whereas even an untutored eye may be held attentive in viewing *The Guns of Navarone* (1961) by that spectacle's emphasis on the pace of its visual stimuli.

A new aesthetic in cinema is possible when motion is recognized as the magic wand that vitalizes and coordinates objects and their subjective meaning. Motion, however, needs to be associated with light for the purposes of recording, interpreting and projecting. Objects obviously need to be luminous in order to be seen. Illumination by itself produces still photography; light alone is static. Since motion is measured rhythms, light, when touched by movement, becomes fluid. Actually, measured motion constitutes the means of shaping and controlling the flow of luminous objects, both animate and inanimate, and also affects accompanying sound and silence. Thus a fresh definition might read: *Cinema is the creation of rhythms amid illuminated objects and accompanying sounds to express meaning and emotion.*

At the risk of belaboring the obvious—which is too often neglected because of its obviousness—we need to be reminded that the optic nerve is the short-cut to the brain, literally and figuratively, because the eye is the thief of all our senses. As an academic and artistic discipline, a law might be proposed—solely for classroom and studio guidance—if a law can be useful in the idiosyncratic practice of an art. Such a law might read: *Visual stimuli in cinema alter in ratio to the rhythms of Motion and Light.*

As a means of examining the cinematic rhythms, their uniqueness and power, what are, first of all, the objects they affect?

Let us first consider the *subject elements of animate and inanimate content*. The human face is potentially the most dominant element in cinema as well it might be in representational forms of the theater, painting, or sculpture. "This communion which is created from time to time, between you and a face, between you and an object . . ."—these words by the Italian director, Federico Fellini, which appeared in the Bolognese journal, *Segnacolo*,[8] are not only a description of Fellini's feeling for his profession, but also of the persuasiveness of cinema. Facial movement, body movement, gestures, and the like are engrossing whenever linked to subjective qualities, which the dual filters of intellectual meaning and sensory experience may register on our consciousness in terms of their narrative, descriptive, informational, or symbolical qualities. The appeal of so-called "stars" is a commercial and a psychological recognition of the power of identification whenever faces become alive through movements. This potential does not apply exclusively to actors, but to all forms of animate life, such as persons in non-dramatic or documentary roles, and the four-footed animals. Such secondary elements as costume and make-up, though influ-

Fig. 1. Violence within the frame created by Akira Kurosawa in *Yojimbo*, 1962. (*Copyright Seneca International*)

ential within themselves, contribute only in association with the movements of actors and persons. Inanimate objects, commonly seen as furnishings and props in interior scenes, and locale, such as exterior scenery, are both subject to the controlling and coordinating powers of visual rhythms. The reality of nature out-of-doors, especially spatial expanses, stimulates the eyes and emotions with special powers; witness classic views of stagecoaches racing parallel to our eyes in trucking shots with or without Indians, or paralleling movements of a character walking while we accompany him, step by step. The identifying power inherent in trucking scenes is a subjective movement which involves viewer and actor simultaneously. These *frame movements,* coordinated with *subject movements,* enhance subjective reactions to the degree of ultimate credibility, or in accordance with the artistic merits present. For example, Richardson's camera-in-a-helicopter shooting of a hunt in *Tom Jones* (1963) (Fig. 2). Motion within the frame is elemental in appeal: Akira Kurosawa is a master in the creation of violence within the frame (Fig. 1).

Aside from subject elements of animate and inanimate content, motion is next evident in the technical elements, known as *light* and *color, size* and *perspective.* To the student of form, the history of maturity is written in the refinements associated with the projection of surface images. Similarly, the student of literary cinema measures development in terms of plot, character, and symbolic evolutions. As for the former, he may easily recall compositional details in relation to light or perspective within a certain shot, and almost as an afterthought list the subjective qualities which actually motivated the whole. Conversely, the literary or dramatic-minded observer is prone to recall scenes, not shots, and discuss in detail emotional or intellectual meanings of character actions and locale backgrounds. The student of cinema should avoid this insidious division into form, subject matter, and content but at the same time be aware of their interrelation. Any resolution he might make in this regard would be facilitated by the degree to which he concentrated on the coordinative factors of motion. For example, what does movement do to *light, color, size,* and *perspective?*

To the student of fine arts, motion is inherent but fixed or limited; fluidity may exist for a fraction of a second. The moment may be aesthetically eternal in a painting or a piece of sculpture, but it is a moment that has been frozen. How much less complicated it is to analyze a representational painting than a representational film. Perhaps one of the motivations of abstract painters is an urge to express rhythms beyond static patterns, such as *rhythms in mass* rather than *rhythm of line;* the uses of color in abstract painting would seem to support this tangential conjecture.

Of the physical elements in a painting, Sir Herbert Read listed five, placing *rhythm of line* first, followed by "massing of forms, space, light and shade, and colour, and this is in most cases the order of their priority—not in absolute importance, but merely as successive stages in the artist's mind".[9] Whatever may be within an artist's unconscious, it is reasonable to believe that rhythm gives form vitality. To continue with Herbert Read: "A form must be defined by an outline, and this outline, unless it is to be lifeless, must have a rhythm of its own." As for the rest: "The massing of forms, space, and light and shade should be considered in close relation. They are all aspects of the artist's feeling for space . . . The Greek architect was always striving to avoid the impression of hollowness, the Gothic architect was always striving to give the impression of immaterial space and airiness. Both were considering together space, mass, light and shade. The same considerations arise in grouping figures or the details of a landscape on the surface of the canvas in painting."[10]

Since vitality in architecture, painting, and sculpture depends so much on *rhythm of line,* how much more vitality is possible when rhythm is extended, as in cinema, to *fluid light, fluid color, fluid size,* and *fluid perspective.* These possibilities—attempted, partially achieved, or fulfilled—are the factors which give a film its evocative excitement. The utilization of variable rhythms creates various times, and thus there can be no absolute time in cinema. This is a challenge to the imagination of directors and writers. For example, a study of the direction of Alain Resnais and the text by Marguerite Duras of *Hiroshima Mon Amour* (1959) should reveal the impact of rhythmic flow upon surface meaning. The picture begins verbally in the words of novelist Duras: "As the film opens, two pair of bare shoulders

Fig. 2. Climax of the frame movements in the hunt shots of *Tom Jones,* 1963. (*Copyright United Artists*)

appear, little by little. All we see are these shoulders—cut off from the body at the height of the head and hips—in an embrace, and as if drenched with ashes, rain, dew, or sweat, whichever is preferred. The main thing is that we get the feeling that this dew, this perspiration, has been deposited by the atomic 'mushroom' as it moves away and evaporates. It should produce a violent, conflicting feeling of freshness and desire. The shoulders are of different colors, one dark, one light."[11]

Resnais translated this by composing images and by editing, both in coordinating rhythms in which light, size, and perspective blended and evolved. Duras's words, "ashes, rain, dew, or sweat", were achieved not in a single phrase, but in a transitional scene of four shots, all medium closeups. In the first, the skin texture of a man's back and a girl's arms is extremely rough; in the second shot, this texture of the lovers' bodies has a bubbly and sparkling quality as though the forms were molded from volcanic ash; in the third, the skin texture has a heavy layer of perspiration; in the fourth, the skin is normal with a slight trace of perspiration (Figs. 3a, 3b). Thus, in these opening shots, movement in the mind of the viewer is created by interrelation in terms of linear perspective coordinated with shade, the interrelation blending and evolving through its juxtaposition of four images. The viewer may see symbolism in sweat turning to atomic sparkles and back to sweat. Resnais composed and edited his shots, relying solely on *rhythms in mass and light* to convey his theme.

In *Last Year at Marienbad* (1961), Resnais conducted his particular orchestration from a text by novelist Alain Robbe-Grillet, and again attempted to transcend time, largely by movements (via editing) back to previous scenes. In spite of surface textures of rare depth, precision, and beauty, the experiment, unfortunately, fails on the whole. The camera travels in trucks and pans to depict a static existence within a massive mausoleum; organ music summons memories of departed encounters. The failure is in the excess of the experiment, the movement after the first half-hour becoming less compelling as the emotional motivations become less precise. The first half-hour has the stylized grace of a chess game; motion is then adventurous, the cuts are like provocative tests and probes, the traveling shots are exploratory. However, when motion comes to depend on the vintage of a woman's gown in order to realize

Figs. 3a,b. Opening shots from *Hiroshima Mon Amour*, 1959. (Photos from the book *Hiroshima Mon Amour*, text by Marguerite Duras for the film by Alain Resnais, New York, Grove Press, 1961)

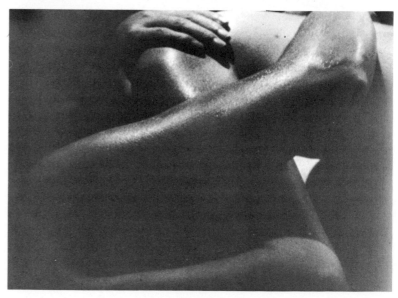

162

past from present, the emotional texture of the film has departed. On the other hand, in *Muriel* (1963) Resnais created a more satisfactory structure through character analysis, so that time itself becomes the motivation.

More successful within a limited area of experimentation, the films of Ian Hugo create multiple motion unlike any ever seen. Motion within the frame is captured and controlled by superimpositions, sometimes more than the eye can consciously record; the whole blends and flows in unique patterns. A painter and an etcher, Hugo as a cinema artist makes color move in association with *rhythm of line* and *rhythms in mass*. His *Bells of Atlantis* (1954) is cinematic poetry, a perfection of mood; *Venice, Etude Number One* (1961) is a masterpiece of motion, visual and aural, utilizing at times as many as seven impositions. *The Gondola Eye* (1963) carries further the experiments in superimposition and equation between image and sound.

In less complicated fashion but more self-conscious of being experimental, Maya Deren, in *A Study in Choreography for Camera* (1945), created "dances choreographed for and performed by the camera and by human beings together".[12] Miss Deren fused motion within the frame with frame motion and both of those with the motion of the cut at the point of the edit. "This film is a dance," she wrote descriptively of *Ritual in Transfigured Time* (1945–1946). "This quality of individual movement, and above all the choreography of the whole, is mainly conferred and created by filmic means—the varying camera speeds, the relating of gestures which were in reality unrelated, the repetition of patterns . . . the film confers dance upon nondancers".[13]

Miss Deren employed *normal* and *slow* camera speeds in recording her images. Camera speeds are variations of subject movement, the motion that occurs within the frame. In cinema, subject motion may be *fast* and *reverse* as well as *normal* and *slow*. In Méliés's *The Doctor's Secret* (about 1900) the use of *stop motion* (trick photography) in coordination with *fast motion* created a new comic fantasy which Mack Sennett later applied to the chase, automotive and ambulatory. Artificial motion can be comic or fantastic, whereas reality is normal motion. Actually, normal frame movements of credible characters, emotionally authentic, can evoke a more intense degree of identification than the same shot done

without trucking. For example, in Malle's *The Lovers* (1959) the frame movements under the moonlight through the trees, over the fields, along the river of the lovers strolling and boating were so exquisitely fluid and sensual that for the first time (half-way through the reels) we believed momentarily in the romance.

"The problem," as Professor Panofsky summarized in his pioneering essay, "is to manipulate and shoot unstylized reality in such a way that the result has style."[14] In that sense, the artist in cinema, for all his command of fabulous motion, is not unlike any artist, described by Picasso during his most abstract period as a man who captures reality, bends it to his will, and sells it to feed his children. The director in cinema has been compared to the conductor of a symphonic orchestra who calls upon sections at certain times, mutes others, blends the whole into an instrument projecting the concepts of the composer and the conductor. Although the cinema director, like the conductor, does present a continuity of performance, I believe that the director is closest in creative kinship to the architect. For all that a symphonic director does, the cinema director must do in terms of plot and landscape, form and feeling, design and purpose—at least, in the planning stage. In addition the director must face a peculiar reality, namely, the architect's knowledge of and ability to deal with contractors (producers and actors), building codes (audiences), unions (craftsmen), and new materials (production values).

What remains to be examined of the objective elements affected by motion is the auditory area: *voice, music,* and *sound.* The intangibles of talent and taste are subjective qualities which affect obviously any application of motion, whether it be applied to animate, inanimate, cinemagraphic, or auditory elements.

Since we see in cinema before we hear, the opposite of traditional theatrical drama, visual motion inevitably affects dialogue, sound effects, songs, background music, and their combinations; often it controls them. In *Citizen Kane* (1941), a gold mine of excellent examples, there is a singing lesson scene between an exasperated maestro and the inept Susan. The shot has an extreme depth of field, similar to a stage setting, in which Susan and the maestro are in the foreground by the piano with Kane in the far background at the door. It is Kane's slow movement forward which intensifies the drama; we await his reaction to the maestro's inability to teach the talentless Susan, Kane's second wife. By the time Kane arrives in the foreground we know that the lessons will continue. Although this example is more dramatic than cinematic, subject motion, by dominating the scene, heightens the suspense. How much more effective when the motion is cinematic. Subsequently, when Susan is on stage opening night the pathos is real. When Kane dies in the opening sequence, the camera cuts from an extreme closeup of the dark lips of Kane, uttering "Rosebud", to a closeup of a glass ball containing "snow" and a miniature house. The movement from one composition to another makes a thematic link, its symbolism being the key to the mysterious word—"Rosebud". Kane's hand relaxes in death, the glass ball drops to the floor and breaks. In this closeup the miniature house is on its side, and, reflected in the distorted glass, the figure of a nurse in white enters where the room is dark. In this combined closeup of the ball she comes forward in the background like a long shot. The cut is to a medium shot from her point of view, in which she pulls a white sheet over the dark face. In these continuity cuts—all in silence since the word was uttered—how death-like becomes the black and white compositional rhythms, unique to this art. Light and rhythm dominate sound in the subsequent satire in *The March of Time* projection room scene. The anonymous reporters are in shadow while the editor, front-lighted (we are shooting at his back) omnipotently orders his men in garbled sounds "to bring back Rosebud, dead or alive".

By panning his camera right and left and reverse, Orson Welles created frame movements which, coordinating with the breakfast dialogue of Kane and his first wife, depicted the decline of that marriage. By trucking in, altering size and perspective, he underscored the credo of Kane instead of relying solely on words and acting; the example of this is a scene in the newspaper office when an outraged Thatcher, lawyer-guardian, is upbraiding his ward. The shot is medium in size, shooting over Thatcher's shoulder at Kane, leaning back in a chair and grinning with pleasure. The guardian's lecture is not unusual nor is it unexpected. Thatcher sits down; there is no cut. The camera trucks slowly into a profile shot of Thatcher, very angry. Now Kane begins to describe his editorial intentions, his face firm, the words aflame: whereupon the camera quickly moves closer, giving a visual force to what Kane says.

There are in *Citizen Kane* approximately 500 shots in two hours, or an average of one shot every 14.5 seconds, all of which attests to an exceptional fluidity, reminiscent in pace to the climactic passages in *The Birth of a Nation* (1915) and *Intolerance* (1916). Undoubtedly the engrossing quality of an action thriller, *The Guns of Navarone* (1961), can be traced to the extraordinary tempo of its editing, executed on an average of one shot every 12 seconds, a total of 763 shots in 155 minutes. Another clue to the power of subject, frame, and edited movements in *The Guns of Navarone* may be found in another startling statistic—though no artistic success is based on a mathematical analysis—namely, that in a script of 157 pages only 89 contain dialogue.

By the above examples I am not suggesting that pure cinema is silent cinema; the utterance of words is normal, though not always wise. Characters in dramatic art forms do talk—"But any attempt to convey thought and feeling exclusively, or even primarily, by speech," Professor Panofsky observed in the early days of "sound pictures" (1934), "leaves us with a feeling of embarrassment, boredom, or both."[15]

Recognition of cinematic rhythms can provide an insightful means for shot analysis.

Of motion achieved through editing, the most common cinematic rhythm is *the cut for continuous action* (continuity). Actually, subject movement sets the pace for this ordinary edit, which in turn generally alters the size of the subject movement in accordance with a shift of locale or perspective. Also, the insertion of a closeup may intensify the flow of continuing time.

Next in frequency of use is *the cut for accelerated action* (rapid or jump editing). This is the motion which contrives to compress less than sixty seconds to the minute, so that action leaps forward beyond normal expectation. These cuts intend to create a feeling of contemporary tempo, especially if the subject movement within the frames lacks dynamic power; such seemed to be the intention of Antonioni in *La Notte* (1961). When subject motion is highly motivated in emotional and visual terms, an accelerated pace that omits the banal and the obvious can have enormous excitement. Witness in *A View From the Bridge* (1962) the scene wherein the niece and her fiancé dance before her incestuous uncle.

Parallel motion permits the viewer to be in two or more places concurrently; this type of editing may be called *the cut for simultaneous action* (crosscut). In the classic ride-to-the-rescue or a classic chase that involves hound and hare, an omnipotence is conferred on the viewer; he may be in two locales at identical times. In Griffith's *Intolerance* (1916), the master of the crosscut had us in four different countries and in four different centuries simultaneously. Time is thematically related by the depiction of historical dramas in which man was intolerant to man; chronological time was ignored. It might be argued that *Intolerance,* thematically, is still ahead of our time. In the celebrated eating scene in *Tom Jones* (1963) the crosscut combined with accelerated action accomplished rare humor and sensuality, exploding in a two-shot climax of subject motion (Fig. 4).

Fig. 4. The crosscut combined with accelerated action explodes in a two-shot climax of subject motion in the eating scene from *Tom Jones,* 1963. (*Copyright United Artists*)

Fig. 5. Through editing of time present and time past in a thematic juxtaposition, a timelessness, like a silent dance, is created in *Last Year at Marienbad*, 1961. (*Copyright Astor Pictures*)

The cut to previous action (flashback) seems to be employed currently for stylistic effect, whereas Griffith used it regularly for simple narrative values. Remembrance of previous actions could be established by having a fade-out on a character, say Elsie Stoneman in *The Birth of a Nation* (1915), and a fade-in on Elsie and The Little Colonel in a tender embrace, a vignette by itself; then back to Elsie recovering from her reverie. The contemporary flashback as utilized by Alain Resnais in *Hiroshima Mon Amour* (1959) and in *Last Year at Marienbad* (1961) more often represents in intent, if not in execution, the crosscutting in *Intolerance;* that is, motion cuts across time and place barriers. Fragments of the French woman's romance with her German lover are inserted now during her embraces with her Japanese lover; the effect, thematically, is an intellectual awareness of a Christian doctrine namely, the love one should feel for one's enemy who is also one's victim. In *Last Year at Marienbad* the sequences involving time previous in juxtaposition to sequences of time present are so intricately blended cinematically that time becomes meaningless; all that appears to matter is a dream-like *motion* that has a mysterious, psychological *flow* (Fig. 5). In this aesthetic sense, the film is successful. The girl X is the sum of her past; likewise the Frenchwoman in *Hiroshima Mon Amour* is the maiden with her young German and the mature woman with her Japanese architect. Past and present are one, Nevers and Hiroshima are one. This is superb artistry, thanks to an imaginative use of the flashback. Fellini's *8½* (1963), influenced in part by *Marienbad,* is a superb demonstration of time past, time present, and time imagined, all interwoven, a subjective *La Dolce Vita,* an unclinical Freudian autobiography, a true masterpiece (Figs. 6a, b).

Finally, the least common cinematic rhythm is *the cut for decelerated action.* Unlike slow motion of subject elements within the frame, time is slowed through editing, usually by repeating parts of previous shots so that a minute seems longer than sixty seconds. Holding back the clock is a technique opposite to jumping the clock forward, which is the method in *the cut for accelerated action.* A classic example of prolonging time through repetitious cuts is the series of shots depicting the descent of a tall fir in *The River* (1937). Nature lovers would wish to hold back time and the tree, and for a few previous seconds Pare Lorentz grants our romantic urge. The crash of the giant tree hence is doubly

Figs. 6a,b. Time past, time present, and time imagined are interwoven by Federico Fellini in *8½*, 1963. (*Copyright Embassy Pictures*)

166

painful. Fragmenting subject movement for the purpose of extracting every drop of emotional or intellectual meaning—a Griffith-Eisenstein technique—may extend time by actual count, but the aesthetic effect can be the opposite. In *Potemkin* (1925), for example, the time it takes for an irate sailor to smash the plate with its lettering, "Give us this day our daily bread", is a matter of two seconds in normal subject movement. By editing this action into nine shots, Eisenstein prolonged the actual motion, but the total impact so stimulated the eye that the doubled lapsed time of four seconds seemed less than two. By deceleration the moment is enlarged, not an unusual psychic phenomenon. Also, laboratory printing may create an illusion of retarded time by slowly dissolving cuts between shots. A posed, inactive shot may also suspend time.

These five basic cinematic rhythms, achieved through editing, coordinate with the equally basic movements of subject motion and frame motion. The effectiveness of any given shot may depend not only on motion within and motion of the frame, but the motion evoked by juxtaposition. Thus, seven fundamental rhythms are responsible for cinema being the art of creating movements. The uses of motion in every shot are based on two—at least subject motion and one of the editing types—or more possible rhythms. The maximum combination would be three: subject, frame, and one of the editing types. These rhythmic concepts may be called *the seven faces of time*. They are obviously not ends, but means employed with subjective qualities. They are not magical numbers that can be imposed arbitrarily, but an empirically valid convenience, useful for critic and creator. They provide a tool for shot analysis, not unlike the means for the scanning of a line of poetry.

Although cinema, more than any art, manipulates physical objects and utilizes machinery, the problem confronting an artist or student is not unlike the constant challenges inherent in the classic arts. Once cinema's uniqueness is more fully understood, we shall have an aesthetic key capable of unlocking new windows.

1. S. M. Eisenstein, *Film Form, Film Sense*, New York, Meridian (1957), p. 57.

2. V. I. Pudovkin, *Film Technique*, Newes, London (1933), p. 53.

3. See L. Moholy-Nagy, *The New Vision*, New York (1930).

4. Erwin Panofsky, "Style and Medium in the Motion Pictures," in *Critique*, Vol. I, No. 3 (Jan.–Feb. 1947), p. 4; first published in 1934 by the Department of Art and Archaeology, Princeton University.

5. Gyorgy Kepes, Introduction to "The Visual Arts Today," in *Daedalus*, Vol. 89, No. 1 (Winter 1960), p. 4.

6. D. W. Prall, *Aesthetic Judgment*, New York, Cromwell (1929), pp. 4–5.

7. William Faulkner, *Writers at Work: The Paris Review Interviews*, New York, Viking (1958), p. 139.

8. Federico Fellini, "The Sweet Beginnings," in *Segnacolo*, Bologna, Italy (August, 1961).

9. Herbert Read, *The Meaning of Art*, London, Penguin-Faber and Faber (1931), p. 37.

10. *Ibid.*, pp. 37–38.

11. Marguerite Duras, *Hiroshima Mon Amour*, New York, Grove Press (1961), p. 15.

12. Maya Deren, *Program Notes*, Cinema 16, New York (1961/1962), Series 15, Program 8, p. 2.

13. *Ibid.*, p. 2.

14. *Op. cit.*, p. 16.

15. *Ibid.*, p. 5.

GORDON B. WASHBURN

STRUCTURE AND CONTINUITY IN EXHIBITION DESIGN

Since the turn of the century, the course of modern art, in its *avant garde* aspects, has been anti-intellectual and anti-humanistic, the long Age of Rationalism having come to a close. This shift of emphasis, signaled by the overthrow of the powers of the national academies, had already been announced in the subjective interests of various nineteenth-century artists, writers and philosophers (e.g., Redon, Proust, Bergson) as well as by the rise of the professional psychologists. For twentieth-century artists the unconscious rather than the conscious now came to be regarded as the central mind, rationalism and the mastery of the will being dismissed in favor of the mysteries of instinct and intuition as arbiters of action.

Thus the Expressionism of Van Gogh was followed by a still greater dependence on subjective guidance in the art of the Fauves, both in Western and Eastern Europe. A certain native classicism lingered in the work of French Cubists, but the Cubist movement on the whole was inherently non-rational, as alone evidenced by a blurring or loss of subject-identification even in presumably figurative canvases. Completely abstract art appeared at this time, followed by the drastic Dada and Surrealist movements which utterly rejected rationalistic thought, and welcomed automatism and an imagery evoked from the unexploited areas of non-awareness. This trend has continued into our own mid-century, as may be seen by perusing any large current exhibition or in the writings of contemporary artists on their art.

One of the most striking changes that has taken place since the close of the nineteenth century now shows itself in the rejection of frames for our contemporary paintings. In an exhibition such as the 1961 Pittsburgh International, frames may no longer be found except where a pretentious dealer has mistakenly hoped to enhance the charms of some costly picture by encasing it in a period molding. The effect is as unhappy as it would be if the President of the United States should be asked to display himself in the garb of Louis XIV. What, we will ask ourselves, does this indicate, and how does it relate to exhibition design?

Until our century, easel pictures in an exhibition required isolation from each other and from their entire surroundings by heavy moldings that often sloped inwards toward the image. Spengler once remarked that the orthodox gold of such frames is a non-color, to be found only outside the spectrum. Because metallic gold is not derived from light—the daylight of reality—it was associated with the idea of eternity. It was employed to indicate that the metaphysical image within must not be confused with a physical reality without. Thus gold came to serve as a warning to the observer to accept what it haloed as a kind of vision, a precious product of mind rather than an extrusion of matter.

To this separatist function of the color we must add another, which is also concerned with the division of things of the spirit from things of the body. Besides the advantage of its non-color, the historic frame, by the nature of its structure, served to separate the internal space of the painting from its immediate environment. Its multiple moldings, like a protective wall, surrounded the spatial artifice within, isolating it from everything else in a different scale—other pictures, actual people, and even the picture gallery itself with its furnishings. Its inward slope, like that of a proscenium arch in the theater, was intended to lead the eye into the spatial depth within, framing a particular view of the world much as a window embrasure invites access to a garden.

We need scarcely remind ourselves that with the recovery of classical thought, Renaissance artists developed perspective, both in its linear and aerial aspects, as the organizing element of their imagery. Transferring to the visual arts the literary unities of time, place and characterization (as derived from classical precepts), artists developed and established the Renaissance convention of apparent reality. This convention presents all the components of an image as viewed from a single position in space and time. In accordance with the logic of this device, painters and sculptors developed a rationale of internal articulations and sequences, joining all of their forms in a seamless fabric of transitions that served to suggest the effect of visual appearances. Thus within the privacy of the frame they provided images parallel to those of the external world. Such a system of visual communication required the use of identifiable symbols—this identifiability being itself part of the logic of the image.

This rationalistic approach, which dominated the construction of works of art from the close of the Middle Ages until the beginning of our century, was the product of the humanistic mind in our Western civilization. A different philosophy is now developing to replace it, one that no longer believes in man as the center of the universe or in man's reason as the supreme instrument of his salvation. A twentieth-century artist, in contrast, seeks guidance from the hidden reaches of thought at the back of his mind, distrusting mere self-awareness and the calculations of his willful ego as reliable guides to creation. He is distressed at the idea of dominating his environment by contrivance and force, and wholly undismayed by the sense of mystery that surrounds him, the profound mystery that had oppressed and burdened his rationalistic predecessors and that all the efforts of science only deepen.

Thus a characteristic artist of our age—such a man, for instance, as Pablo Picasso—delights in embracing the wonders and terrors of a universe that cannot be understood, developing a supra-logical art to express his vision of reality. Such men do not regard themselves as the authors of their art. They maintain instead that they are disciplined yet submissive vehicles through which forces of nature have their outlet and expression. Braque begs us to omit the title of "master", explaining that he is not the master of his own work, whose images insist on taking their own shape in accordance with forces that lie beyond his calculations and control. When a work is done, all vestiges of his original intentions have disappeared and the new work is as great a discovery for the artist as for us.

Another representative artist, Jean Dubuffet, welcomes and reverences all manifestations of reality, however vulgar, ugly or savage they may be, incorporating them into a whole-natured art that rejoices in its material inclusiveness. In a very real sense, the barriers between vision and reality have evaporated in the view of life that these artists offer, and their images need no longer be fenced off from the rest of creation by self-protective frames. Things of the spirit and things of the body are no longer seen as separable and distinct. Space is one.

When pictures in the Renaissance tradition are exhibited, their heavy frames permit us to hang them closely together and even in vertical tiers, one above the other. They may be crowded as much as we like, just as they were formerly crowded on palace and museum walls until the turn of the century (Fig. 1). Each one is seen as a self-contained image (provided the distance is not too great for us to "read" it) whose inner scale and character are isolated from the next by the formal intercession of its frame. To further separate such works, extra framing was often provided—as it still is in the National Gallery in Washington, D.C.—by means of the architectural moldings that panel the galleries.

So long as figurative elements were kept, scale could be maintained within the picture, even when it was distorted by subjective deformations, as in Picasso's *Guernica*. But with the development of nonfigurative paintings, it became evident that the scale of a picture must now be found in relation to the observer, as in the case of the works of the New York school of Action Painters. Inevitably such paintings increased in size, the size of a human being becoming the determinant of scale, all thought of their utility to apartment house dwellers being regarded as irrelevant. Not being conceived in terms of illusionistic depth, they could readily expand in surface dimensions; instead of deepening, they could spread. Moreover, the tendency to enlarge was also fostered by the need that was felt to increase our awareness of their concrete reality as organic entities—that is to say, as imagery that is independent of all direct reference to actualities in the outer world. Each picture was regarded as being in itself such an actuality, and therefore self-sufficient.

With this intimate relationship established with the observer, frames could be regarded only as obstructions. Their continued use must inevitably force the picture back into its isolation as an art form instead of allowing it equality with other natural products of life. Now, frameless, the painting functions as part of the very space within which the observer himself stands (Fig. 2).

This change of feeling and usage already led to the novelties called *papier-collé* and *collage* in the first decade of the twentieth century, innovations that have more recently developed into a form known as "the art of assemblage". As they are of a nonrational character, the products of assemblage belong to no conventional category, being neither paintings nor sculpture but partaking of each. With the dismissal of Renaissance conventions as used in works of a classical order, the character of these new images has been transformed, becoming simply "works of art" without any categorical name.

So it has transpired that assembled art has scavenged and absorbed into the fabric of its being concrete fragments of actuality that are commonplace to our daily experience of urban life. The ugly chaos of our city streets must somehow be converted into images of perfection without denying their vulgar substance. Such an artist of assemblage as Robert Mallary of New York regards himself as an "abstract realist" who unites the reality of trash and junk with the reality of thought and feeling to produce a super-reality, within which conflicting elements from his own inner and outer worlds are harmonized and resolved. The actual materials of urban disorder and disunity thus appear in his work as a mask which veils yet reveals the perfection he offers. By this means, he dissolves an apparent dualism (i.e. actuality and vision) without resorting to abstract media such as oil paints or clay. By the word "abstract" in "abstract realist" he clearly means both "concrete" and "nonfigurative" since it is not his intention to offer references to nature even though they may be discovered in the final image.

The resultant work of art does not ask to be isolated from other objects in a room, but only to be sufficiently freed from them to be seen. How shall it be used, then, lacking as it does the logical apparatus of the frame or the architectonic logic of the pedestal? Whether we want to or not, we are likely to use it in the highly rational setting of a museum's gallery, or even try to hang it in a Georgian-style house, in spite of its denial of classical values. And if we use it in the pseudo-Renaissance setting that most museums provide, will it fit this Procrustean bed if it is hung within a series—that is to say, as if we were planting a Renaissance parterre, row on row? Fit it must, and what is worse, we will crowd it up next to its neighbors, hanging it along with other works that have been picked for their sympathetic character, just as a hostess seats her dinner partners.

Fig. 1. Gallery at Carnegie Institute, Pittsburgh International Exhibition, 1898.

Fig. 2. Gallery at Carnegie Institute, Pittsburgh International Exhibition, 1961.

1

2

Because of the new accessibility of the contemporary image to the spectator (both, as it were, standing in the same space), there are many who suppose that modern pictures can be made to mingle intimately with each other when hung in an exhibition. They presume that framelessness and accessibility invite us to merge these works, making so perfect a harmony of relations that the entire exhibition becomes in itself a work of art. This is to misunderstand the nature and function of any creation, whether old or modern. It is true that the contemporary artist seems to want to destroy barriers between his work and the world of the observer, but it is not true that he offers the same view of reality as those of his colleagues. What he offers may not be egotistically conceived, but it cannot fail, if original, to give us a view of truth that is his own. After a passage of years it may be observed that his work clearly belonged to his age, but it will also be evident (if he has been a great seer) that he opened men's eyes to a unique view of reality, one that he had seen for himself.

For this reason, it would seem evident that we who install mixed exhibitions of modern art must make sure that the exhibits may be seen independently. Ideally, each work should have a separate area or compartment in which to hang, but this is seldom feasible in the limited space that is available. We merely attempt, therefore, to install each sculpture or picture in such a way that it does not become overly confused with its neighbors and that it succeeds, so far as may be possible, in standing on its own feet. This is not easy when there are no frames to separate the images, and it becomes a great temptation to put things that have common attributes together so that a group of works will merge in a series that is superficially harmonious (Figs. 3, 4). British things, for example, will invite contiguity by their Britishness, and whitish pictures by their common tone. Texture, too, will attract texture, and geometrical forms will too easily melt into one another if they are put close together.

By rights there should be a very considerable expanse of open space between one work and the next, but the extensive amount required usually seems so wasteful that arrangers cannot bring themselves to sacrifice it. As a result, merging is resorted to, and visitors will often offer compliments that should not be taken as valid, the easy effect of continuity and harmony that was achieved being a serious fault, not a virtue. The supreme compliment for such an erroneous hanging, which asserts that the combined pictures and sculptures form a single work of art, must be regarded as the most unacceptable of all. This implies that the works of art on exhibition are being used not for themselves but for their effect within an ensemble, each work a kind of brick that is used to build a beautiful wall or a single note of color that finds its place in the assembled picture.

Artists whose works are so misused have every reason to feel distressed, a feeling that we understand has actually been expressed by several painters, including Rothko and Still, who have done what they can to prevent their paintings from being hung beside the work of others in group shows. Whereas a certain continuity of spirit may be expected within an artist's own *oeuvre,* in a mixed exhibition it is not helpful to allow pictures to bleed into each other. In these circumstances an harmonious effect is accomplished at the expense of the life energies of the paintings, and each suffers a kind of castration by contiguity.

We must conclude, therefore, that discontinuity rather than continuity must be the ideal in group exhibitions. This can be accomplished only through a generous use of space, even when a row effect has been successfully avoided. Inasmuch as rows of pictures automatically produce the illusion

Fig. 3. Pittsburgh International Exhibition, 1958.
Although harmonious and spacious, this installation errs in combining items that bleed into each other. Not only the forms, but also the whiteness of these works falsely unites them at the expense of the individual statements.

Fig. 4. Pittsburgh International Exhibition, 1958.
A section of modern assemblage: here four expressionist paintings are juxtaposed to effect a unified hanging at the expense of individual content. The value of the individual works is blunted and devitalized by the bleeding of one picture into the next.

3

4

of a related series, many organizers of modern exhibitions are careful to destroy this effect of continuity as often as possible by hanging pictures in informal balance rather than on a single parallel eyeline (Fig. 5). When the single line is unavoidable due to the excessive number of works to be shown, arrangers will attempt to stop the tendency toward a merging of each picture with the next by an adroit use of contrasting works that arrest the sense of flow and isolate each one from its neighbor (Fig. 6).

To conclude, nothing will serve so well as complete isolation for each work of art. Arp calls works of art the fruit of men, noting that each human being produces his own variety. Being unique creations, they cannot be compared with one another any more than we can compare the qualities of the apple with the pear. Neither can we add to them or subtract from them with impunity. The fruit of Miró is not to be confused with that of Matisse, inasmuch as each is the creation of a singular organism. It is for this same reason that graded prizes do violence to the very nature of the individual work of art, there being no way of designating the first, second, and third pieces in an exhibition if each is a unique creation.

5

Fig. 5. Pittsburgh International Exhibition, 1958.
This hanging is preferable by its juxtaposition of contrasting images which separate the individual works, allowing them to seem harmonious up to a point, yet permitting them to stand alone.

Fig. 6. Pittsburgh International Exhibition, 1961.
Even though the right-hand painting (Canogar) is not wholly visible, it is clear that each of these pictures lives independently on the wall, although certain color harmonies unite the ensemble. This independence is due as much to the contrast among the works themselves as to their spacing; they are apart as well as together.

DONALD APPLEYARD

MOTION, SEQUENCE AND THE CITY

As the pace of travel quickens, and the cities continue to spread, motion increasingly saturates the urban experience. It is evident in the painter's brush stroke, the blurred photograph, the movie of urban life. And each day, most of us, by one mode or another, travel through the city. It is not always a pleasant experience. Clutter, congestion and hazard see to that. But there are moments and there is a potential for great delight. Motion can bring a sense of freedom, vividness and power to city travel. It can enliven a dead scene. And it plays a primary role in the formulation and communication of the city image,[1] its structure and meaning, for the city is apprehended as we move within it.

How can motion be built into the design of cities? The environmental designer has found it easy to talk about, but difficult to manipulate. Ephemeral yet ubiquitous, it is elusive to capture, record and therefore design. Let us begin by looking at the various ways motion may serve our purposes, the effects motion may have on our *awareness, mastery,* and *understanding* of the city.[2]

MOTION AWARENESS

To generalize about the motion experience is a dangerous task, for perception is infinitely variable. Each person sees the environment in a slightly different way. His background, familiarity with the place, purpose, mode of travel or role within it, can make the same situation unrecognizable. Time, traffic, and climate impart their own variations to the scene. Yet there are broad areas of perceptual agreement about the environment, and we shall try to keep at this general level.

The observer selects and organizes the perceptual world through his senses. He can enjoy it at the purely sensory level; identify it structurally for purposes of orientation; or he can read meaning into it. His attention may be directed toward any one of these tasks or it may ignore the scene altogether, concentrating on social, personal or other matters. If he attends, his awareness, orientation or understanding may increase. His response may be emotional, attitudinal or overtly active. His sense of freedom may be enhanced or destroyed.

Our perception of motion, whether it be our own motion or that of the field, may differ substantially from what is really in motion, for apparent motion depends primarily on perceived displacement. A parallel moving vehicle may appear to be static in relation to one's own car; the vehicle ahead may seem motionless within the environment. Such mild illusions occur constantly in city travel. Two further conditions for the perception of motion are the perceived rate of change and duration of perception. The flow of a river, or the growth of a city can only be observed when successive percepts are apparently displaced against remembered configurations.

Self-Motion. Self-motion and environmental motion, apparent and real, constitute our motion world. Awareness of self-motion, a primary concern, is important not only for our general sense of well-being, pleasure and stimulation, but for our very safety as we move about the city. The measures of self-motion—velocity, direction, and distance—can be appreciated through several senses—visual, kinesthetic, tactile and auditory—varying with the mode of travel. The more correlation there is between these sensory cues, the more accurately can our own motion be judged. Frequently they fail to match, and even in combination they may fail to support an accurate estimation. Speed may be miscalculated, direction confused, distance apparently compressed or extended. Such perceptual ambiguity usually inhibits our operating efficiency.

The kinesthetic sense of body movement predominates for the man on foot. He is nearly always aware of his sharp and jerky walking movements. Changes in pace, shifts in direction cause redistributions of weight and balance in the body. Uphill tasks or long journeys bring on fatigue. But, once he climbs into a vehicle, the whole variety of personal movements, in which our language is rich—dawdling, strolling, walking, stepping, hopping, running, or climbing—become restricted. He sits, perhaps operating the gears, with movements that bear only an indirect relationship to his travel. The passenger is even more out of touch. In the well-sprung automobile, only definite stops, pronounced acceleration or retardation, sharp bends or inclines are kinesthetically apparent. With closed eyes on the limited access highway, only a slight vibration is felt. Motion has steadied, changes in direction have been graded out, stops are eliminated. The passenger, and even the driver, may sink into lethargy, or ignore the environment altogether. The automobile or any other closed vehicle screens out many tactile cues of self-motion. The feel of surface texture, like grass, cobbles or asphalt, microclimatic change like gusts of wind, radiant heat, or cool shadow, and the brushing past of other people, are eliminated. Constant temperature, the radio, or conversation remove us from the surroundings.

The man on the freeway depends more on visual cues to sense and estimate his own motion. Relieved from the nagging attention of cross-traffic and pedestrians, the necessity for accurate estimate is not so obvious. He feels freer to look around, contemplate the passing environment, and enjoy the grace of his own movement. Rapid absorption of the paved surface, the radiation and growth of the field ahead, the flick and blur of roadside features, and movement of the whole landscape, tell, in varying degrees, of his progress. Again, they frequently tell different stories. His apparent speed will be accentuated by the passing of foreground objects, diminished if only the far landscape is seen. Sensations of floating or suspension are not infrequent on elevated or cross-country freeways. Accompanying traffic too is disconcertingly stationary, with only the rear lamps to tell us when the car in front has slowed down.

Once down the off-ramp and onto the city street, the erratic movements of traffic and pedestrians force judgments of self-motion to be more accurate. Less time can be spent on contemplating slow change when at any moment a child may appear from behind parked cars. Snapshot glances cover both central and peripheral fields. Judgment is not easy, demanding conscious, though unwilling, attention. Apparent self-motion increases with foreground events and enclosure, and the driver is forced to slow down through overload. Real motion becomes sporadic, things never seem to get under way, and frustration sets in. Even the bus passenger cannot wholly avoid the misery.

For the pedestrian, this problem is not so severe. He has others. Frequent concern for his own next step still makes him highly attentive to foreground path problems. Changes in floor surface keep his eyes close to the ground, for fear of a twisted ankle. Avoidance of street furniture and other people is necessary, but serious hazard only occurs when he has to cross in front of other traffic. For relief, he is able to seek the relaxation of an uncrowded stroll on a stretch of grass where he can shelve for a while the pressures of self-navigation.

The visual sense is essential for its predictive value, and its accuracy of judgment. In city travel, the ability to predict one's own movement and that of others is gradually acquired. A man from the country, a stranger in a new city, or a driver in a new vehicle acts clumsily, while the habitué, proudly at home in his environment, moves easily, with split-second timing and assurance.

Path and vehicle are the twin generators of self-motion. Erratic path alignment, or a random staccato of crossings can be harsh and disturbing, while the arching rhythms of Venice, the swinging sidepaths of Amsterdam canals, the stop light continuity of New York avenues, or the humping movement of the New Jersey Turnpike are satisfying and distinctive path experiences. A powerful rhythm sets up a sense of continuity.

While harmony of movement may be one aim of a successful path, drama is also part of the experience. Certain movements of the path acquire the personality and animation of individual movement. Like a movie camera, it can approach, search, hesitate, leap at or avoid features of the environment. It can indulge in self-expressive movements, like jumping, twisting and turning. A whole sequence of movement can unfold like a dramatic plot with explorations, setbacks, surreptitious glances and final conquest. This semblance of life in the path seems to depend on the complexity of its movement. A straight path has a dead quality, a curving one begins to come alive.

The vehicle may heighten or reduce the sense of self-motion. Though the screening out of motion cues and the suppression of energy sources has brought a gain in smoothness, speed, and comfort, vehicular travel has lost much of its sense of adventure and meaning. Only the rare excitement of the cable cars in San Francisco, the Staten Island ferry, or a ride in a pony and trap hint at the rigorous pleasures of earlier travel.

A city or even a country may be characterized by the vehicles that it uses. The gargantuan smoothness of the modern American automobile differentiates the United States from Europe, but also Caracas from Rio de Janeiro. And when the city acquires a new type of streetcar or subway train it becomes rejuvenated.

Apparent Motion of the Environment. When the observer moves, the environment is set in apparent motion. Mass, space, light, surface and detail pass by in continuous transformation. More evident and delightful on the freeway or from the tracked vehicle, where motion is continuous and relaxed, the environmental field appears to be in vast rotation, diminishing in velocity from foreground to background. Motion clarifies and articulates the field. Foreground blur moves across the background, objects loom up, swing and turn, each facet revealed like some gesturing mannequin, and complex movements of the road can throw the entire scene into a choreographic wonder.

177

The environment gains personality in the same way that the path comes to life, for the movement of objects is often interpreted to result from motor forces.[3] A foreground mass may wipe out an enticing view, one transparent sign can rake over another, landmarks may fall into line, buildings unfold. City towers can dance across the roofs, the conveyor belts on East River Drive seemingly unwrap the United Nations building on approach. The rotation of circular objects is notably satisfying. Santa Maria della Salute turning in domical splendor along the Canale Grande or the more common revolutions of gas tanks, oil refineries, and silos are harmonious and unthreatening; whereas long buildings perpendicular to the path may seem to rise up like wielded clubs.

Motion through space leaves an even stronger impression. The trauma experienced on entering tunnels or other very confined spaces and the sense of release, surprise and delight of entering a new space, indicate the force of these sensations. Confinement usually induces a heightening of experiential intensity; openness conveys a sense of serenity. Each can be satisfying, if not in excess, but long tunnels, corridors, serpentine paths or the obsessive openness of some expressways and suburban streets can bring on claustro- or agoraphobia.

Other qualities of the channel also shape the experience. Spatial definition of the path—planted trees, a safety curb, a hip-high wall or hedge—grip the traveller reassuringly, while he may seem to slip off a curbless track. The surface of floor and enclosure, if powerfully textured, may convert a visual sensation into an apparently tactile one. Concrete walls scrub, scratch and brush past. The patterned sidewalks of Rio heave and swell like the ocean. The "fill" of a channel may also influence its character. Parked cars and trees define a sidewalk space. Traffic can clog up an otherwise well defined street.

At points of spatial transition expectation and vulnerability become acute. Architects employ welcoming eaves, and the Greeks used colonnades to break down the wall between outside and inside. The kind of transition, its gradient and complexity, can spell the success or failure of a spatial experience. The stepped entries into the Piazza del Campo in Siena focus one's eyes solely on the floor, before allowing them to rise and apprehend the space, while a view presented blandly loses most of its intensity. Cuts, dissolves, merges and wipes can be as effective as in the cinema.

At times, the whole visual world may seem to move or shift about the observer. Directional changes in confined spaces, like the clover leaf turn of a modern expressway or a rondpoint, can cause giddiness and disorientation. Though frequently unnerving, such contrasts may bring life to an otherwise dull journey. The more stable the world, on the other hand, the greater the opportunity for perusal of the landscape, a useful attribute when a complex view demands detailed study. In the longer term, movements take place in the overall city image. Centers rise, intensify and move. Suburbs creep, jump and sprawl across the landscape. Here the shifts in attention from old to new give the appearance of motion, the equivalent of stroboscopic movement. The inhabitants may be in real migration, but it is the physical form which seems to move.

Real Motion of the Environment. From the very first phases of perception, when the child discriminates objects by their movement, things in real motion, particularly one's fellow human beings and the machines they manipulate, as well as other signs of their activity, attract his attention. Actions of other pedestrians or drivers are carefully watched, by the cautious for surprise movements that might threaten personal safety, and by the bolder ones as potential obstacles in the path ahead. The pedestrian may also hope to meet a familiar face, while the stranger searches for similarities and differences from his past experience.

The movements of people and traffic, milling, gathering, swarming, pouring or weaving, or birds flocking and swooping, can transform a city space. It will spring to life. Visual interaction is an important form of social interaction. In bigger cities, people can be seen in crowds, in smaller cities individually, but while city centers are still the places to find activity, in large parts of our urban environment we are witnessing the disappearance altogether of visible people. The freeway, the suburban street, and commercial strip, though filled with flashing lights, are empty of human faces. Only the automobile is left as a sign of its owner's presence.

Nevertheless, if well designed, an automobile can make a graceful sight on the modern highway, and at night, when its form dissolves into red and white lights,

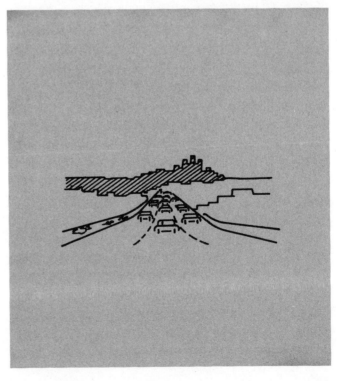

it can gather with other vehicles into snaking trails of fantasy. The sight of movement on another system can also be a source of pleasure or surprise. The rare appearance of a railroad train, a truck crossing an overhead bridge, a ship, helicopter or airplane attract attention, however small they may be in the scene.

Visual impressions of real motion can be amply reinforced with noise and vibration. A bus bearing down on a bus stop, or a truck careening down a hill, are not easily forgotten by a pedestrian in their path. At times only the noise of motion is apparent. The eerie siren of a passing police car, the overhead whine of an airplane, a screech of brakes, the clap of horses' hooves, though not so accurately perceived, are often more vivid than visual cues of a motion event. Most impressive of all is the combination earth-shaking, smoke-belching, light-flashing, angled take-off of a large jet aircraft, for here the source and reality of motion are made manifest in one heroic event.

A more indeterminate yet pervasive movement in the city is that of natural and climatic forces. The listlessness of Venice, the falling rain of Manchester, or San Francisco's rolling fogs, not to mention the tremor of an earthquake, are phenomena which a designer cannot ignore. In many climates, every movement of the air is a blessing; in others, protection is of paramount importance. Ways of increasing awareness of either may be a welcome comfort. The Japanese hang glass and bamboo mobiles to accent through vision and sound the coming of the breeze. The windmills which mounted the walls of old Dutch cities must have been a telling indicator of climatic change. Today we rely on the temperature and humidity signs, or the wind-blown trash that covers the streets.

While climate may impart a unidirectional movement to the city, for instance its trees may bend all one way, over-all patterns of movement can be discerned in the commutation and migration of its inhabitants. The cues which tell us of these movements are restricted mainly to the people and vehicles themselves. Traffic thickens as the rush hour nears. New faces signal the arrival of a new group in the neighborhood. These patterns are not seen as a whole, they are deduced from fragmentary information. If we wished to articulate them more clearly, perhaps for the sake of general information, several techniques might be possible. Build-

ings could visibly rise and fall, paths swell and shrink as their occupancy changed. The city skyline could ascend in the morning and sink in the evening. Mobile houses could move with the migrants just as the suburbs appear to move today. Such extremes may, however, be unnecessary. Clearer exposure, lighting and signing of these flows and migrations could achieve some of this clarity.

Signs and Symbols of Motion. Traces and other signs of motion echo its drama. The polished walls of Tiryns recall vividly the passing of men three thousand years ago. Worn steps, road ruts, jet and smoke trails, tell that motion was there. Flickering networks of street lamps trace out the pattern of a dark city. Gradients of age, scale or pattern reveal the direction of historic flow.

The forms of movement channels, footpaths, streets, railroad tracks, and canals to the flight and swirl of elevated freeways, or the leap and thrust of bridges, express concretely the purposeful quality of travel. Architects have found this encasement of movement a rich source of dynamic form. Since the futuristic sketches of Sant'Elia and before, the vocabulary of ramps, steps, covered ways, elevator towers has been ever on the increase. And, in soaring verticals, in streamlining or the graceful flight of the concrete, movement is the dominant expressive force.

MASTERY THROUGH MOTION

Motion plays a vital role in our mastery of the environment. Self-motion is itself a demonstration against the earth-binding weight of gravity. If we climb or fly, our defiance is greater. The feeling of independence is precious for the individual in our society, yet in the course of his movement about the city he lives in a precarious balance of power with his environment. Control and choice over his own movement, its speed and rhythm, the lack of obstacles to his progress, and his position in space all affect his perceived freedom.

The pedestrian retains the highest degree of personal maneuverability. He may stop, look around, reverse his steps, in fact, carry out an endless number of operations. But restrictions on his freedom are on the increase. Confined more and more to sidewalks and street crossings, and kept off the grass, the independent jaywalker may soon disappear. We may have to learn from the Japanese the art of guiding personal movement. In their gardens a rocky path, a cross-lapped bridge, a set of stepping stones can lead the stroller through the steps of an intricate dance.

The limits of pedestrian speed and stamina confine his scope to small areas of the city. He may also be oppressed by the vertical bulk of surrounding buildings or the horizontal scale of its paths. If the environment shows no sign that it can be used by him, or is intended for him, he feels out of scale, ignored. The endless repetitive streets of suburban areas, the broken sidewalks and asphalt deserts of drive-in commercial streets are not for him. In the American city today only a few central places and some old neighborhoods maintain extensive interest for the man on foot.

Automobile movement is more regularized and therefore, in many respects, more restricted than that of the pedestrian. Confined to a bulky vehicle and a defined channel, errors are difficult to correct, stopping and starting require great care, and self-control, though not always evident, is in constant demand. While the obstacled progress of a city street accentuates these difficulties, the freeway reveals fully the automobile's compensating virtues. Speed and continuity, frequent elevation and extensive panoramas combine to give a sense of freedom and power previously unknown to the ordinary citizen: a point to be considered by those who see the automobile and freeways only as a menace. Large parts of the metropolis, whole cities, are brought within the traveller's grasp. Far distances are compressed, disparate features juxtaposed. But even on the freeway, the traveller has to struggle for survival. More lanes and heavier traffic diminish his apparent size and importance. Path alignment or the passing scene may fall out of scale with his movement, choice of channel or speed may be restricted, and he becomes a cog in the machine, a number in the engineer's computations.

The vehicle, its size, speed and maneuverability can increase or diminish the sense of control. When it acts as an extension of the individual, as in the automobile, or motorcycle, his sense of power increases markedly. If this power is unaccompanied by an awareness of self-motion, a dangerous psychology, common among car drivers, can build up. For the transit passenger, on the other hand, the feeling of control does not exist. In the railroad train, subway, ferry or ship, the impersonal movement leaves him unaware of the piloting problems. He can read a newspaper, gaze out of the window, or stroll the deck. But the bus or aircraft passenger is constantly reminded of being in someone else's hands, as the driver attempts to negotiate traffic or the pilot tries to get the plane off the ground. Helpless yet involved, his journey can be very uncomfortable.

Each mode of travel has its own control and scale limits. An interesting motion sequence for one may be an anathema to another. An expressway can be a desert for the pedestrian, the crowded street speaks congestion and overload for the driver. The mixing of movement in common channels can therefore create perceptual difficulties. Though a channel cannot be perfectly fitted to the speed and scale of its movement, there is an optimum range of congruence, beyond which a scale breakdown may occur.

ORIENTATION AND UNDERSTANDING

As he navigates through the local and general environment, the traveller is engaged in a strategy of search. While the commuter can check on his pre-formed image, noting any new changes, the visitor is in constant danger of getting lost. The path ahead is of immediate concern. Any clues as to its future direction, or signs of a future destination, are picked up and become goals, whose sighting, approach and attainment may be noted with some excitement. These goals may be elements of the path itself—bridges, intersections, street corners, stairs—or they may be important features of the city image—church spires, skyscrapers, a river or the ocean.

Frequently a goal is transformed or disappears on approach. Such transformations occur particularly with skyscrapers whose silhouettes bear no perceivable relation to their bases. The failure to arrive is a constant source of dissatisfaction. When a goal is revealed for a long time its impression may begin to fade. We lose interest in it. If, however, it temporarily disappears, or is partially masked, attention, even anxiety returns at the threatened loss. Its presence has become conditional rather than assured.

The scope of goal sighting depends on foreground obstacles, on the openness of the route, and on velocity of travel, which tends to project the eye further ahead when speed is increased. On the expressway goals may be sighted many miles away, becoming familiar over long stretches of the road, while on the city street the path ahead is more of a mystery. Traffic, confinement, and directional changes limit the view. The higher rate of surprise, a delight of the medieval city, may compensate for disorientation, but in excess may be baffling.

Goals may overlap or succeed each other. A set may be introduced at one viewpoint, then singled out individually, or several minor goals can play against a major one. Path and city goals may occur in rhythmic alternation.

Orientation to the path itself depends on more than goal structure. Since any path may be entered at several points and travelled in either direction, a sense of position and directional differentiation is essential. Most arterial streets lack both these qualities. Old distinctions have become blurred through the uniformity of signs, lighting and street furniture. Natural variations have been smothered. One intersection looks much like another, to be remembered only for the slightest of differences, like the sign of a gas station, or the shape of a piece of curb. The image of such a path slips around our minds as we try to grasp its structure.

For the transit passenger, of course, transfer points are the strategic moments of decision and orientation. The clarity of their internal structure is of paramount importance to him. The clear connection of the path to the immediate surroundings is a problem with transit and freeways, floating as they do in the city image, while the pedestrian path and city street, enmeshed as they are in the local environment, face the converse difficulty of clarifying location in the larger context.

In all cases, the widest exposure of major city and natural elements, the radiation of their presence through signs and symbols, the location of major paths in proximity, coincidence, or intersection with them, and the exploitation of prominent viewpoints, will assist in orientation. The placing of freeways along the water's edge or along river beds, though often spoiling natural features, does clarify the view from the road. The city street gains by passing through activity centers, an asset which closure for pedestrian malls will eliminate.

How can motion and sequence help the traveller to understand more than the visual structure of the city?

How can it be made more meaningful? The elements of the visual pattern should at least correspond to the elements of the functional, physical and social pattern. In the past, for instance, important buildings have looked important. They were often located in commanding and visible positions, approached via boulevards and driveways, by long and tiring flights of steps, and were fronted by forecourts. Temples, cathedrals, palaces, city halls benefited from an appropriately significant visual approach. Today, important buildings, even City Hall, may be stumbled upon in a moment of surprise. Not many visitors, for instance, know where New York's City Hall lies. The really fine vistas are appropriated for the nation's advertisers, whose astute knowledge of city visibility and perception deserves closer study.

Exposure of activity is another way of revealing the city's meaning. The sight, sound and smell of market places, railroad stations, and cities in warmer climes tell us what is going on, while we learn very little from the blandness of modern suburban developments.

Finally, motion itself may communicate the quality of a place. The serpentine drives of Central Park express its rustic contrast with the gridiron city, a bumpy road suggests its use by heavy trucks.

SEQUENCE

Travel through the city creates a sequence of experience. This sequence is a moving encounter with the environment, in which the traveller acts according to his own purposes, while the environment reciprocally shapes his experience. If we describe a sequence as a succession of events, each event, set against the remembered past, will affect the traveller's attitude, response and perception of the future. Thus each experience is relative. A dark space, entered from a darker tunnel, may seem very bright. Past, present and future are joined.

What makes a good sequence? The satisfaction of the various travellers' demands. A sequence may be enjoyed purely as a sensuous dialogue with the environment, or it may be used to glean information about the city, its structure and meaning. Desire and need tend to characterize the former attitude, prediction and expectation the latter. Both may be found, sometimes simultaneously, in any sequence.

The prolongation or repetition of any experience brings forth the desire for change. Without it our senses atrophy, but contrast gives life to a sequence. It may be a sharp change in the scene, a shift in scale, a different material, a change in direction or a new view. If trivial, it is ineffective, if excessive the thread of continuity may be broken. Several sudden changes, and we have entered another world, another sequence. If breaks like these occur randomly throughout a journey, the city will be imaged as a set of disconnected pieces. Continuity can be maintained by consistency of motion, space, surface or other features, by repetition, similarity or overlap. Rhythm, a primitive and powerful sequential organizer, can bind the most diverse of experiences into a coherent order.

At the more cognitive level of orientation and meaning, the traveller is engaged in a strategy of search, a guessing game at which the commuter is a practiced player. Information is received when there is a mismatch between prediction and answer.[4] It is therefore equated with surprise, and, though in urban design surprise is normally employed to describe the effect of contrast, we take it here to include this broader function. Familiarity with a route will cause marked differences in perception and attitude. The first-time traveller, predicting with only those cues he can glean from the landscape, will be highly attentive to any information relevant to his goal. He will need a certain level of redundancy to ensure against being lost, and not until he seems to have completed his necessary schema will he relax and enjoy the trip.[5] The commuter, on the other hand, sure of his prediction, may absorb all necessary information subliminally. His active interest is roused only by unpredictable traffic movements or new changes in the environment. In the case of either traveller there will be some comfort range for the rate of surprise outside of which overload, frustration or boredom may ensue. If the information bears no relation to that previously gained, the sense of progression is lost. The careful construction of a coherent city image, the qualities and functions of a river or lakeshore revealed successively from different vantage points on a freeway, or the spatial structure of a path intensifying toward the city center, could supply the connecting theme.

Surprise is emotionally neutral. If no change is expected, it may be a delight. If an important climax is anticipated, disappointment may ensue. The pattern of expectation, desire, satisfaction and disappointment is the rhythmical basis of sequential form.[6]

The beginning and end of a sequence demand some consideration. One may ask how much of an entity an urban sequence can be when it may be used in numberless ways. Yet beginning and end are different from middle. The first contact, like the meeting with a stranger, strongly determines future attitude. Anticipation is high and with the conclusion of a sequence, a sudden disappearance or a fadeaway may leave the participant feeling empty and cheated. A sense of arrival, resolution or fulfillment is needed, for the journey without destination is a difficult one to make. Introduction and conclusion, for every entry and departure, though seemingly unachievable, should be the aim.

Finally, since an urban sequence is used by countless different people, with varying attitudes, purpose and familiarity, a choice of structure will be necessary. Information might be patterned at different levels for different purposes. It may be coded to avoid overlap and inconsistency. Some may be revealed only after repeated journeys, unfolding with increased knowledge. But only essential messages should be so insistent that they cannot be excluded. The traveller's privacy should not be assaulted.

Sequences may be structured in various ways to meet the above objectives. The organization of *sensuous form,* the sequence of *image disclosure* or, at a more primitive level, the *structure of attention* seem useful ways of describing them.

Sensuous Form. The sensuous form of a sequence is derived from the succession of motion, mass, space, light, surface detail, activity and goals. Though in the contemporary city these qualities seldom form successful combinations, some bright fragments, half-submerged patterns, can be discerned. Constancy or change characterize each quality, forming homogeneous sectors or regions, changing gradients, and more abrupt transitions. Sectors may be homogeneous in any number of aspects; direction, speed, spatial proportion, activity or traffic intensity, detail, surface, continuities of vegeta-

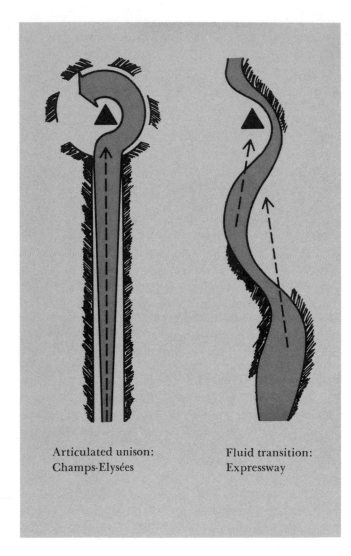

Articulated unison:
Champs-Elysées

Fluid transition:
Expressway

tion, terrain, or building type. Gradual changes of activity intensity, height of enclosure, width of channel, or the approach of an important goal, form gradients. Bends, stops, spatial contrast, cross traffic, goal arrival are frequently markers of transition. While the homogeneous parts may set the general character of a sequence, the points of transition attract the highest attention. Contrasting experience, new information, a possible decision, may make them the more memorable parts of a journey.

The definition of a sector, or the power of a transition depends on the reinforcement or clustering of several component qualities. The Champs-Elysées, for instance, maintains a continuity of direction, motion, spatial proportion, building height, façade, and vegetation, while the path slowly rises toward the approaching Etoile. On arrival at the goal, changes in direction, pace, traffic, space, and enclosure occur simultaneously. Like some grandiose march, the whole system strides across the city in articulated unison.

The coincidence of constancy and change among components is however only one form of structure, as music amply reveals. Variation, exposition, development, even counterpoint may be possible, and each mode may give rise to a different sequential form. On the expressway, for example, we encounter more fluid transitions. On the city street and subway sectors break up more definitely into components.

Image Disclosure. The second quality of sequential structure has to do with the sequence of information being disclosed to the traveller. This may be practical information on how to get around, building up his image, or deeper information about the meaning of the city, its function, history or social structure, its personality or values. The path experience, in this case, may be likened more to a novel or a film, where the plot is essential to the shaping of a cogent message. A plot provokes curiosity, maintains interest, and fulfills anticipation. But, more than a story, it emphasizes causality, or the lack of it. The disclosure of information is purposeful and dramatic. Themes of conflict and resolution, the influence of context, or the revelation of character are inherent in its structure.

The analogy to a city path becomes clear. The arousal of expectations by the glimpse of a future destination, the backward look over a path traversed, prophesy or recall. Radiation of view from a small intensely felt fragment to a whole scene, the technique of *pars pro toto* adopted by film directors from literature,[7] occurs in many framed approaches. The care with which the Greeks revealed the form of their temples from the processional way is another instance worthy of study.[8] Mystery and surprise, recurrent themes in dramatic form, are sensed in the goal structure of many city sequences. A look, therefore, at other more developed arts may well be of use to the sequence designer until he has his own collection of good examples.

Structure of Attention. The intensity structure, notable in city as well as other sequences, is the most primitive summary of the above experiences. The tempo and rhythm of attention appear to be measures of it. Attention oscillates between necessary concern with the path ahead: traffic, decision points, hazards, and environmental changes; the sighting of, or arrival at dramatic and meaningful features of the city. The interplay between attention to path and to environment may form one of the basic rhythms of a journey. When the level of attention rises too high, the traveller compensates by slowing down, another variable which increases the difficulties of intensity measurement, but which allows a greater intake of events at climax points in the city.

The general intensity structure of a journey may be constant, increasing or decreasing. A sequence with variations about a constant level of intensity would be characteristic of a circumferential city route, which never arrives at a major center, but intensity increase to an ultimate climax is the classic sequential form. Variations can elaborate the basic gradient. It may be stepped up, retarded or premature, as indeed occurs in the approach to many cities. Boston's North East Expressway in a series of increasing climaxes crests several hills, each marking more clearly the approach to the central city. Tunnel entries and confined arterial approaches frequently retard the climax, while a panoramic preview forewarns the traveller of what is to come. The decreasing, anticlimax, or departure experience may be the most difficult to deal with. Its attraction lies in the sense of relief after intensity, typical of the homeward journey or escape to the wilderness. It is a beginning rather than an end.

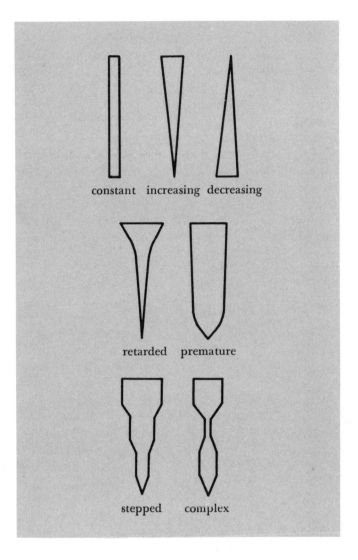

constant increasing decreasing

retarded premature

stepped complex

To summarize, a good sequence, like any work of art, must be a created synthesis. Rich, coherent and expressive, it should enhance the traveller's awareness of and pleasure in his own motion and that of the environment. It should encourage his sense of mastery and independence, and increase his understanding of the city by clear orientation and meaningful exposure. To achieve this, contrast and surprise must be developed within a pattern of continuity, progression, and fulfillment, structured at several levels for interruption, reversal, and repetition of experience, for the variant needs of the different travellers. We have hardly begun to understand what this may mean.

SEQUENCE SYSTEMS

One day, we may entertain the outrageous idea that every possible journey through the city be part of a total system of sequences. Each path would be shaped to allow for interrupted and reversed journeys. From the footpath outside the front door, to the elevator and corridor of his place of work, our citizen could have the choice of a stimulating, meaningful and changing experience. Contrasting alternative routes, urban or rural, intensive or relaxed, classically ordered or loosely structured, would be at his command. Though the possibility seems remote, the computer, given a more explicit language and purpose, may come to our aid, by extending the designer's hand.

To move about the city with ease, the traveller needs a clear image of the system he is on, of other systems and of the city. The coherence of each system, differentiation of paths and intersections within it, and clarity of connection to other systems are essential. Although an individual may use only a part of his system, he may at any moment have to extend his knowledge. Its image should be easily available for recall. Orientation problems like these differ between systems. For the driver, retrieval must be instantaneous, while the transit passenger has more time. Navigational difficulties increase for the driver as the choice of routes increases; the city street system is the most complex to unravel.

There are two distinct ways of organizing a sequence system: either through the system itself, its paths and connections; or by orienting the system to the city en-

two-way grid

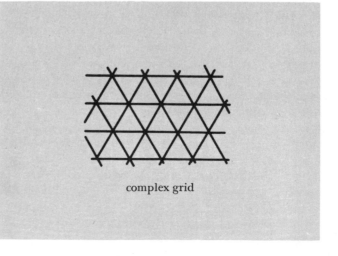

complex grid

radial system

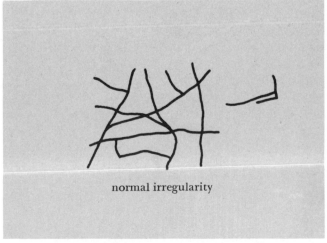

normal irregularity

vironment, to major destinations or other features of the city. To clarify a system, the creation of a map pattern, which can be immediately recalled, is a good beginning. A two-way grid is the simplest pattern, and topological variations can be accommodated so long as directions at intersections remain consistent. More complex grids, though allowing more direct, general accessibility, suffer from the complexity of crossings. In Washington, drivers are forced to adopt special techniques of recognition to negotiate the six-way intersections, and Market Street, San Francisco, the meeting point of two grid systems, acts like a fault line across the image structure. The radial system with its multidirectional spokes, and curving circumferentials, though more ambiguous than the grid, does maintain the same simplicity of intersection. None of these patterns alone can solve the problem of orientation, however, for they only distinguish routes by direction. But their systematic method of connection can serve as an outline for reference.

Current cities seldom display any of these patterns in pure form or over the whole city. They are rich in disjointed, wandering and disappearing paths, ambiguous and inconsistent junctions, and wrong priorities. A delight for the seasoned inhabitant, who alone can unravel them, they are meaningless and aggravating to the majority. Also, movement systems like those in Europe, New England or many suburban areas are so random and yet entrenched that all efforts to reduce them to a simple network may be defeated. Other kinds of system organization supplementary to or independent of the map pattern are needed.

Developments of the above patterns might include hierarchical or dominant sets of routes, but the repetition of these routes will result in a number of streets and intersections whose form will be identical. Distinctive patterns of intensity, sensuous character or disclosure will be necessary for their differentiation. The slow rhythm and wider cross-section of New York avenues provides contrast with the cross-streets, an improvement on the regular gridiron city. Channel width, confinement, façade, floor surface, the kinds of activity, the form of signs, planting or street furniture may also provide this distinction. In such a system all A routes may be roughly east-west, all B routes north-south.

Organization through city image:
approach to differentiated activity centers

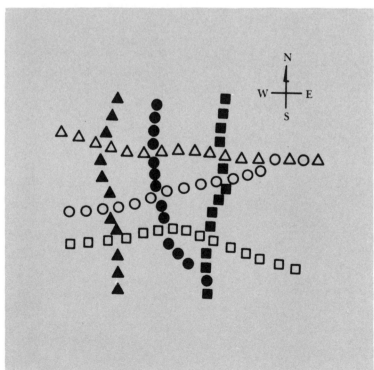

Organization through system image:
route differentiation.

In cities that have grown slowly the character of paths is built-in rather than applied. It would be difficult to confuse Whitehall, Charing Cross Road, or Oxford Street, but in rapidly planned cities like Brasilia or Chandigarh, or in mass-produced suburbs like Levittown, the problem can be acute. Interchanges, the strategic points of decision in any system, demand even more attention to their patterning, differentiation, and clarity. One intersection looks like another in the gridiron city, while in other systems, clearer differentiation is often accompanied by directional confusion.

Organization by reference to the city image may play an alternative or supporting role in system design. The intensity and rhythm of path structure, for instance, could increase toward major activity centers. The dominance of downtown has helped to differentiate many movement systems, but its influence wanes with the increasing spread of urbanization. All routes may also bear the character of their destinations or approaching features. Thus the approach to the entertainment district could be gaily lit, tree-lined streets hint the arrival of a park and fountains signal the presence of water. Exposure and clarity of the city image is the obvious and essential counterpart to this effort.

Maps and verbal signs are often proposed as the solution to city orientation, but they have limitations. Subway travellers, forced to rely solely on these aids, are caused some anxiety if the window fails to stop in front of the station sign. The man driving a vehicle cannot easily pause to consult his map, and if he misses the sign an error is not easily corrected. Besides, verbal signs can carry only a limited message of poor accuracy. The expressways, relying solely on verbal signs when they can be visibly oriented to the city, are missing a valuable reinforcement to the clarity of their system. There is no substitute for actually being able to see one's destination.

The knitting together of the different movement systems is of primary importance. The isolation, for instance, of freeways, subways and railroads is a real source of confusion in the city image. Connection or transfer points play a crucial role here, often acting as entry or departure points to and from the outside world. The humble bus stop, parking lot and off-ramp, the subway station, railroad and airline terminal, creating moments (sometimes hours) of raised anticipation, alertness, and decision, even of joy or sadness, need clear and visible connection to each system and a well oriented internal organization. Mixed channels, route intervisibility and clear signing also reinforce system coherence.

Redundancy and choice of organization may be as useful guidelines for system design as they are for sequences. Each system then may have two or three overlaid patterns of order, a set of simultaneous alternatives, so that travellers with differing sets may choose the structure they find most meaningful to them. If one pattern fails, another can come into play. These different patterns of organization exist partially in the city today. We need to learn more about them.

NOTATION

The city designer cannot go out into the city and move it around with his bare hands. He works with symbols, and therefore needs an appropriate language for recording and creating motion and sequence. If expense and time were no limitation, an organization with equipment to make cineramic films and animated cartoons would be ideal. These methods may become more accessible with the use of computers. As things are, the handiest tool is still the drawing. But the architectural drawing, though useful to capture the physical reality, is inadequate for the setting down of perceived reality. A language using experiential symbols is necessary. It must be a language easily learned, and therefore as close in form as possible to the original experience. Musical notation is too abstract. Choreographic notations, like the early Feuillet language, are closer in spirit, though confined to self-motion. Some examples of attempts to analyze and design sequences with a new language[9] are illustrated here. Plans and sections are still the primary media used, although increasing knowledge of sequences may enable us to read structure more clearly through perspective series.

Conclusion. Many aspects of motion, especially its functional and social implications, have been passed over in this essay. Whole systems have been omitted, the opening world of new ways and styles of motion has hardly been explored. Too much is still speculation. Experiment, measurement, and design are needed, but first of all we must tune in our senses to the complex delights of "seeing" motion as it is. For too long we have talked only of form and space.

4

3

CASE STUDY:
SEQUENCE DESIGN IN A NEW CITY

This is a hypothetical design for a spinal highway through a new industrial city in eastern Venezuela.* Though based on assumptions that have subsequently changed in the real situation, it indicates diagramatically a way in which the design of a major highway sequence can organize the pattern of a city. The plan of the urban texture shows this highway threading through the city on an alignment parallel to the Orinoco River, terminating in industry at both ends, with the city center astride the Caroni River, just below the Caroni Falls. The climate is tropical, the breeze from the east, and the housing—much of it inevitably self-help—is located on the hill slopes overlooking the two rivers. The plan shows the principal characteristics which would distinguish the housing areas.

For reasons of simplicity the sequence diagram is drawn separately from the urban texture diagram. Its alignment is indicated by a motion band, which swells when the road is elevated and shrinks when it is depressed, thus describing the path of travel in three dimensions. Only features visible from the path are diagramed here. Long views are indicated by arrows issuing from the road, spatial change appears in the form of cuttings, overhead bridges, hills, etc. Movement is from west to east. The principal aspect of sequential organization is the rhythmical shifting of direction which quickens as the road descends toward the city center. Coordinated with this movement are views of successive sub-centers approached on axis, then by-passed on alternate sides. On each of these straight stretches the towers of the main center are seen over the skyline of the local center. The plateaus which the road must traverse are wide and uninteresting with the exception of some small outcrop hills. The route uses these as anchor points to define its own location. The diagonal changes in the direction of the route allow contrasting cross-views out over the valleys and rivers on either side. Thus the main entry and work route for the city would be clearly aligned, well oriented to the focal pattern of city centers, and yet offering a clear sense of the relation between the two rivers and the falls. Besides this it holds the potential of being a stimulating visual experience.

2

1

The accompanying photographs looking eastward show: 1) a typical view along the western plateau; 2) the current entry into the Caroni Valley from the west; 3) an aerial view of this same scene with the Caroni River in the middle distance and the Orinoco in the background; and 4) the ferry crossing.

*The city of Santo Tomé being planned by the Guayana Development Corporation with the assistance of the M.I.T.-Harvard Joint Center for Urban Studies. This design, part of a student project, is by George Kurilko, M.I.T.

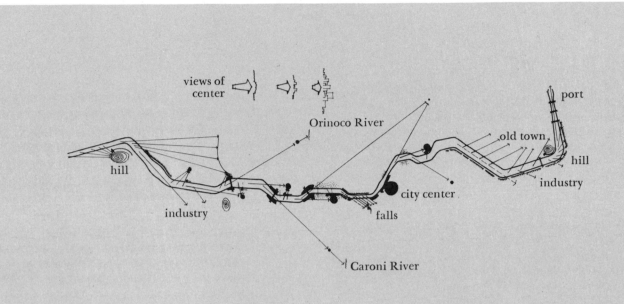

SEQUENCE DIAGRAM

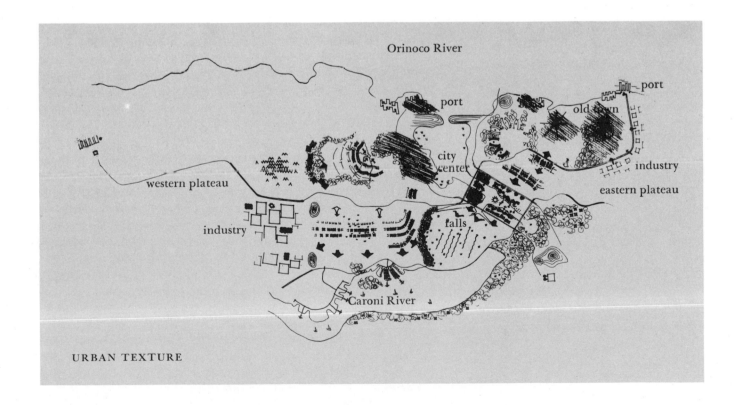

URBAN TEXTURE

1. Kevin Lynch, *The Image of the City*, Cambridge, M.I.T. Press (1960), pp. 95–97.

2. The writer is co-author of *The View from the Road*, Cambridge, M.I.T. Press (1964) with Kevin Lynch and John R. Myer, to whom he is indebted for many of the thoughts presented here. The M.I.T.-Harvard Joint Center for Urban Studies is sponsoring this research.

3. See Michotte's movie experiments explained in Rudolf Arnheim's *Art and Visual Perception*, Berkeley, University of California Press (1954), pp. 321–329.

4. Predictive tests made by C. E. Shannon on the level of redundancy in the English language, may indicate a method for measuring the informational input on urban sequences.

5. Jerome Bruner, "On Perceptual Readiness", in *Psychological Review* (1957), Vol. 64, No. 2, explains a possibly analogous strategy of search in perception.

6. I. A. Richards, *Principles of Literary Criticism*, New York, Harvest (original edition 1925), Chap. XVII.

7. Sergei Eisenstein, *Film Form*, New York, Meridian (1957), p. 132. (Original edition 1949.)

8. R. D. Martiennsen, *The Idea of Space in Greek Architecture*, Johannesburg, Witwatersrand U.P. (1956), pp. 117–149.

9. The language developed in *The View From the Road*, Cambridge, M.I.T. Press (1964).

BIOGRAPHICAL NOTES ON THE AUTHORS

James S. Ackerman

Art historian. Born 1919. Studied at Yale and New York Univ. Taught at Yale and Univ. of California, Berkeley. Since 1960 Professor, Dept. of Fine Arts, Harvard. Major publications: *The Architecture of Michelangelo* (1961); co-author, *Seventeenth Century Science and the Arts* (1961); with Rhys Carpenter, *Art and Archaeology* (*The Humanities in America*) (1963).

Donald Appleyard

Architect and urban designer. Born London, 1928. Studied architecture at the Architectural Association, and city planning at M.I.T. Practiced architecture and planning in England, Italy and the United States. Since 1961 Assistant Professor, Dept. of City Planning, M.I.T. Co-author with Kevin Lynch and John R. Myer of *The View From the Road* (1964). Currently working at the M.I.T.–Harvard Joint Center for Urban Studies on the visual form of sequence systems, and on the design for a new industrial city in Venezuela.

Gillo Dorfles

Aesthetician and art critic. Born Trieste, 1910. Professor of Aesthetics, Univ. of Trieste. Former editor of *Aut Aut* and *Domus*. Has lectured widely in Europe and America. Major publications: *Discorso tecnico delle Arti* (1950); *Barocco nell'architettura moderna* (1951); *Le oscillazione del gusto* (1958); *Il Divenire delle Arti* (1959); *L'architettura moderna* (1954 and 1962); *Ultime tendenze dell'arte* (1961); *Simbolo Comunicazione Consumo* (1962); *Il Disegno Industriale e la sua estetica* (1963).

Karl Gerstner

Artist. Born Basel, 1930. Trained in graphic, typographic and photographic domains. Since 1953 has been producing interchangeable and serial (programmed) pictures. His works have been exhibited throughout Europe and are represented in public and private collections in Europe and America. Writings: on interchangeable and serial pictures in *Spirale*, No. 5 (1955), No. 8 (1960), and in the book, *Programmiertes Entwerfen/Designing Programmes* (1963); on the sources of serial art in *Kalte Kunst* (1957/63). His ideal is the production and distribution of pictures on an industrial basis, and consequently a social art, an art for everyone.

Robert Gessner

Professor of Motion Pictures, New York University, since 1941. Founded first four-year curriculum in Liberal Arts leading to a degree in motion pictures. Founding President, Society of Cinematologists. Founding director, The Motion Pictures Foundation for Colleges and Universities. 1962–63: Ford Foundation grant to produce series of experimental films at Harvard in association with I. A. Richards. Author of many books and articles; has lectured widely in United States and Europe.

James J. Gibson

Psychologist. Spent war years as Air Force psychologist working on problems of depth perception in aircraft landings and on the use of pictures and films. Since 1948 Professor of Psychology, Cornell Univ. Author: *The Perception of the Visual World* (1950). Now writing a general treatment of the use of the senses for perception. Experimental research on visual perception and on the knowledge obtainable from pictures has convinced him that the classical conceptions of seeing and perceiving are inadequate and that a new approach is required.

Stanley W. Hayter	Painter and graphic artist. Born London, 1901. Since 1927 his paintings and prints have been shown in innumerable exhibitions in Europe and the United States. Works represented in more than sixty museums throughout the world. A most important figure in the re-establishment of printmaking as a vital and creative art: in 1927 founded, in Paris, Atelier 17, a workshop where artists work together developing and sharing their ideas and discoveries in the field of printmaking. Author: *New Ways of Gravure* (1949).
Gerald Holton	Professor of Physics, Harvard. Born 1922. A student of P. W. Bridgman, he received his Ph.D., Harvard, 1948. Combines experimental research (properties of materials under high pressure: ultrasonics) with teaching and studies in the philosophy and history of science. 1957–63, editor of American Academy of Arts and Sciences and founder of quarterly journal, *Daedalus*. Currently general editor of new series, *Classics of Science*. Major publications: *Introduction to Concepts and Theories in Physical Science* (1952); *Foundations of Modern Physical Science* (1958); *Experimental Physics* (1954); *Science and the Modern Mind* (1958).
Gyorgy Kepes	Painter and designer. Born Selyp, Hungary, 1906. 1930–36 worked in Berlin and London on film, stage, and exhibition design. In 1937 came to the United States to head the Light and Color Department, Institute of Design, Chicago. Since 1946 Professor of Visual Design, M.I.T. Author of *Language of Vision* and *The New Landscape in Art and Science;* editor of *The Visual Arts Today*.
Katharine Kuh	Art critic. Studied at Vassar College and Univ. of Chicago. 1936–43: Director, Katharine Kuh Gallery, Chicago, specializing in contemporary and experimental work. 1938–40: Professor of Art, Univ. of San Miguel, Guanjuato, Mexico. 1946: member, mission to study Indian totemic carvings, Alaska. 1955: Ford Foundation grant, developed series of adult discussion groups in modern art. 1956: organized American Exhibition, Venice Biennale. 1953–59: Curator, Art Institute, Chicago. Since 1959 Art Editor, *Saturday Review*. Author: *Art Has Many Faces* (1951); *Léger* (1953); *The Artist's Voice* (1963).
Hans Richter	Painter and pioneer in experimental film. Born Berlin 1888. Studied Weimar. 1916–18: Zurich, member of Dada movement and studied counterpoint with Feruccio Busoni. 1919: with Viking Eggeling began experiments discovering principle of continuity of formal elements leading to the scroll form and abstract film. 1921–27, scrolls and films: *Rhythms 21, 23, 25,* abstract films; *Film Study,* film using abstract and natural forms; *Ghosts before Breakfast,* Dada film. In 1928 began intensive activity as film director, producer and theoretician while continuing activity as painter—these two interests complementing each other throughout his career. 1940 settled in United States, becoming Director of Film Institute and Professor, City College, New York, and member, American Abstract Artists. 1944–57: great scrolls and many single paintings, as well as the films, *Dreams that Money Can Buy* (with Léger, Duchamp, Man Ray, Max Ernst and Calder), *8 x 8, Dadascope, Chess Cetera.* 1948–62: Comprehensive exhibitions: San Francisco, Berlin, Rome, Zurich, Amsterdam, Essen, Munich, etc.

George Rickey   Artist, writer, teacher. Born South Bend, Ind., 1907. Studied modern history, Balliol College, Oxford. Studied also, Ruskin School of Design, Academie Lhote, and Institute of Fine Arts, New York Univ. Began work as teacher and painter. Presently Professor of Design, Rensselaer Polytechnic Institute. Since 1949 has devoted himself to sculpture in motion. 1961–63: Guggenheim Fellowship for studies in the physics of motion as applied to creative sculpture. His sculptures have been exhibited throughout the United States and many European cities. Works represented in many American museums. Currently preparing for publication an important book, entitled *Heirs of Constructivism*.

Hans Wallach   Psychologist. Born Berlin, 1914. Ph.D. Univ. of Berlin 1935. At Swarthmore College since 1936, where since 1953 he has been Professor, and currently Chairman of the Department of Psychology and Education.

Gordon B. Washburn   Museum director. Born 1904. Studied at Williams College and Harvard. Director: 1931–42, Albright Art Gallery, Buffalo; 1942–49, Museum of Art, Rhode Island School of Design, Providence; 1950–62, Department of Fine Arts, Carnegie Institute, Pittsburgh; and currently Director of Asia House Gallery, Asia Society, New York City. Has written many exhibition catalogues and articles for various art and museum journals. Organizer of many important exhibitions, including the Carnegie International Exhibitions of Painting and Sculpture.

Designed by the arts staff, George Braziller, Inc.
Printed in offset by Connecticut Printers, Inc., Hartford, Conn.